Living in Beauty

Healing Experience of Transformation

BY JOSEPH KURIAN

EMC Publishing
San Francisco, California

LIGHT
Spirit

CLARITY
Mind

ENERGY
Body

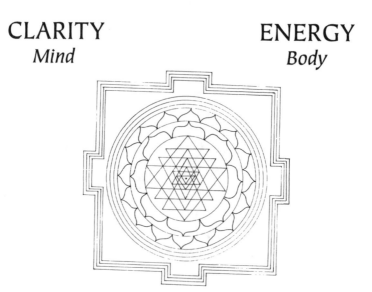

~Enchanting charisma

~Delightful charm

~Graceful allure

***Within you, and only within you, calmly awaits
your perfectly balanced, beautiful self . . .***

*In my experience, the state of our physiology determines
our character. When our physical, mental, and emotional imbalances
are corrected in the physiology, the resulting change in character
is enough to change our destiny.*

—*Joseph Kurian*

Since universal energy lights all our lives, it is no coincidence that what scientists are now calling bioelectromagnetism is essentially what ancient India developed over time as Marma Science. The oral traditions of India preserved the precious wisdom of biotechnology long before the Age of Technology.

Living in Beauty describes how our subtle energy body defines the quality of our life and offers ways to naturally stimulate the body's energy field for protection, health, and beauty.

A certain vibrational resonance on all levels of our being is required to stay in balance. The key is the crossroads where energy and matter converge, called *marmas*. Beauty is created here — not only in appearance, but in vitality and expression.

Joseph Kurian shares his gift of rejuvenation through natural stimulation of the body's electromagnetic field. The universal energy source is available to you with the right information. In your hands is a concise account of traditional energy techniques and a sincere understanding of joyful, harmonious life.

Ayur Veda	*Marma Science*	*Rejuvenation*
Dhanur Veda	*Kalaripayat*	*Kaya Kalpa*
Breathing	*Mantras*	*Meditation*
Beauty	*Health*	*Longevity*

Joseph Kurian was born in Kerala, India, where he began to study and apprentice with traditional masters of Ayur Veda, Dhanur Veda, and Marma Science. He is also a proficient expert in the elegant martial art called Kalaripayat and the ancient, yet advanced, longevity science known as Kaya Kalpa. After studying the cultures of twenty countries and working with ten thousand clients, his uniquely formulated and effectual products and programs have attracted an international clientele in the United States, England, Italy, and Monte Carlo. Joseph Kurian is now based in California.

EMC Publishing
2185 Fifteenth Ave.
San Francisco, CA 94116-1844
Web Site: http://www.marma.com

Note to the reader: This book was written to convey informative and instructional guidelines. The methodology, techniques, and remedies outlined within the book are not intended to replace professional medical attention. For any serious condition, consult a qualified physician or health professional.

Drawings of flower and mandala by Rudiger Dahlke and Katharina von Martius from **Mandalas of the World** ©1985. Used with permission of Sterling Publishing Co., Inc., New York

Drawings of hands in mudra positions by Susana McGuire ©2000.

Library of Congress Cataloging-in-Publication Data:
Kurian, Joseph
Living in Beauty
ISBN 1-893279-00-6 CIP 98-90929

Published 2000 by EMC Publishing, San Francisco, CA

TABLE OF CONTENTS

Preface

Within each of us lives the potential for absolute beauty, health, and vitality. Beauty is more than merely physical in nature. It is also energy, passion, expression, and grace of movement. Beauty springs forth from our innermost being when there is a balanced merging of body, mind, and spirit — a trinity of energies that interlace in a synergy that is *you.*

Physiological blockages can occur in the organs, which in turn affect our psychological state and then go on to influence our vitality and spirit. Imbalances are reflected in our appearance and our personality. It is simple — when we do not feel good, we do not look good. When we are out of sync with our basic nature, our lives reveal a lack of rhythm and energy, most especially in our appearance.

The correlation between beauty and health is the foundation of the rejuvenation sciences of ancient India. The techniques and formulas for attaining beauty through balance were regarded as sacred and invaluable. The royalty was fully aware that ultimate beauty comes from a strong life force flowing through clear energy channels. Kings and queens kept the practitioners of these arts and sciences close at hand throughout their lifetimes.

The sacred wisdom embodied in the practices of rejuvenation has been passed along from one master to the next in each generation. I have been fortunate to be entrusted with continuing these healing and rejuvenating traditions; I hope you will enjoy the opportunity to learn how to remove obstacles and thereby open endless possibilities.

Please see figures 1-3 at the center of this book
[Photos of Joseph with Master]

My birthplace is Kerala, India — historically a cultural center for the ancient *Vedic* Sciences, which are traditions dating back twelve thousand years. These sciences contain the original energy medicine and complete knowledge of revitalizing the human form. *Dhanur Veda* is one of the most fundamental of all the traditions — the Science of Defense, or strength on the battlefield. In the evolution of the Vedic Sciences, Dhanur Veda predates *Ayur Veda*, although there are themes common to both. Herbalism, for example, developed in each of the two sciences with various formulas. The study of energy balancing evolved in both, each science exploring different aspects of the same universal principles.

Dhanur Veda is a full complex of sciences, with ancient techniques that involve the achievement of strong willpower, intensive physical training, and mental prowess. From the war sciences of Dhanur Veda came a potent form of Marma Science — **electromagnetic current stimulation** — in the study of life force energy and energy centers. The warrior's tradition had evolved into a healing art.

Marma is the pathway to accessing the universal energy that generates and sustains life in all its creative beauty. Marma brings energy, vitality, longevity, and beauty to life. Marma offers strength and stability of mind and emotions, freedom from doubts and limitations of the past, and an open awareness of a higher spiritual understanding. Marma Science and Dhanur Veda culminate in *Kaya Kalpa* — the wisdom of rejuvenation.

I have always had a great curiosity for acquiring knowledge, which served me well in extensive studies and disciplined training with various masters. Beginning at the age of nine, I had access to excellent Western methods as well as the traditional Indian modalities. By the age of twenty-five, I had reached mastery in the traditional sciences of India.

Expanding my years of training with my own research into the various patterns of people in different countries, I have developed a signature system of health and beauty — MARMA SKINCARE — a convenient self-care system of herbal creams and teas. As a vehicle for the herbal energy, it provides the ability to clear energy channels of blockages, repair marma damage, and restore homeostasis to the physiology. By reestablishing a natural state, the life force flows freely, energizes the body, stimulates the mind, and enlightens the spirit. On a more intensive level, my REJUVENATION & LONGEVITY PROGRAM is unique in the world insofar as I have adapted the sophisticated techniques of natural laws to the needs of contemporary society.

In my products and programs, the same finely-tuned, transformative energies that once were used to treat the royalty of ancient India are now properly conducted for modern people. In my years of practice, I have worked with over ten thousand clients around the world. After leaving India, I established a beauty clinic in Paris, where I adapted the techniques to enhance people's appearance. The exceptional glow of rejuvenation has also attracted clients in Milan, London, Monte Carlo, Japan, and Mexico.

In this book, I would like to share the basics of this knowledge of Marma Science with you, so that you might also enjoy the health, beauty, and vitality you deserve. The rare formulas and unique energy modality are constantly evolving according to changing influences and cultural patterns. From the original energy medicine of Dhanur Veda, through all the other sciences and research, I have extracted the most essential truths and intuit their application in my practice.

Science explains the laws at work but does not operate as a creative principle. The art of well-being is accomplished when a master practitioner knows how to assist the healing powers of Nature. This evolution of Marma Science that I bring to you is a singular version from the most ancient, powerful variations. My life is dedicated to creating a system of natural stimulation with electromagnetic current, or EMC.

It is my privilege to have learned the practical applications, my honor to have the intuitive ability to understand the interconnection of the energy body and the physiology. People always ask me, "What about this? Why do I have it?" I am able to address their individual situation from my research and experience. Since I have been in the United States, I have observed different varieties of problems and worked with them in my practice. When clients become better, their gratitude makes me feel a great compassion to continue searching for deep, incisive solutions.

INTRODUCTION

Please make yourself comfortable. Relax in your favorite chair. I would like to tell you the story of Marma Science as it has been related to me by my predecessors.

There are aspects of our world that are timeless. This pure Indian tradition dates back as far as the beginning of recorded knowledge. The wisdom of *marma* holds the understanding of these triangle-shaped energy centers, universally interconnected in a vast triangular energy pattern, and individually interwoven throughout the human body. Marma Science has been kept alive in an oral tradition since ancient times; its principles still apply to us today. Our minds and bodies are different from those of our ancestors, but our spirits (or souls) are the same. The same life force energy that flows within us also connects us universally through marmas.

It has been a blessing to be able to study, learn, and refine this ancient wisdom. The past fifteen years of my research and personal hands-on experience have helped me to organize this information. Many of these subjects you may never hear about again or read about in any other book. The special teachings set forth in this book could only be found in the most closely guarded oral traditions of ancient India, until now.

The knowledge of marma is considered sacred. As my master who taught herbalism said, "Marma has been kept secret for thousands of years. I have seen so many students, even those from my own family, and I have not been able to find a person who can spread the knowledge of marma in the right way. Everything has to be done with a respectful manner, for only then will the effect be there. Otherwise, a very strong energy effect will be missing; there will only be the herbs. There will not be any Soul or Life with energy power to go along with the herbs. You, however, will be able to spread the knowledge of marma to the world in the proper manner."

Indian Tradition

The Vedic masters with whom I apprenticed instilled in me the purity, validity, and power of the Indian traditions. The herbal formulas they entrusted to me are invaluable, as are the formulas from the tribal healers who practice timeless arts of wellness. I spent many years studying the Vedic sciences and the Indian martial arts.

There is some correlation among the Indian sciences, as well as between the Indian sciences and such disciplines as modern reflexology and acupuncture. However, they can all be traced back through history to the Indian traditions.

Fifteen hundred years ago, a great Buddhist monk came from Kancheepuram in Talminadu, South India. Like Siddartha, he had been a prince. Bodhidharma had been taught the ancient medicine along with Buddhism and the Indian martial arts.

Setting out into the world, he traveled along the Silk Road to spread Buddhism throughout Asia. He also conveyed the medical modalities and martial arts which, over time, were adapted into many other systems — acupuncture and Oriental martial arts, for instance. Since then, these traditions have spread out all over Asia in different forms, but the fundamental concepts and understanding of the marma system are still found in the original form in southern India.

If you observe the Indian culture, you will notice an extensive use of body ornaments and jewel tattoos. These are not only for decorative purposes, but, more importantly, for medicinal purposes of stimulating marmas in daily life. For example: wearing gold jewelry on the side of the ear stimulates the spine; wearing gemstone jewelry on the earlobes prevents illness; wearing jewels on the nose helps one to sleep better. Nowadays, jewelry is considered decoration for women, but in India, it has been worn by men and women up until the last generation. Every part of India has recognized this common practice of preventing illness, which we do not find in any other part of Asia.

India was once divided into thousands of countries. Now it is unified, but each of its cultures retains its own knowledge and standards. My home state on the Malabar Coast in South India is one of the oldest centers of traditional learning. At the midpoint of the old spice route, it has historically played an important role in the sea trade between the Western and Asian worlds. The finest quality herbs and spices were carried by European traders to the West, along with tales of the Eastern traditions. As a result of these traders, South Indian culture spread out in different forms — from the Greek and Roman eras through the commercial expansion of the Dutch, Portuguese, English, and Arabs.

Inspired by the knowledge of energy relations, the people of India have been able to cooperate even with different religions and cultures. Their standard of living has evolved along with the cultivation of the ancient Vedic sciences. To examine their system of community is to realize that all aspects of society are coming from the same energy concepts as in the ancient marma system. With economic equality for everyone, production of their own food, financial independence, and a balanced state of health and beauty, the paradox of having a good standard of living without much money is due to the harmonious cooperation of the people and their ability to live conscientiously, valuing their resources.

South India is a place of paradisiacal beauty with incredible mountains, lakes, and sea. People are very interconnected with Nature. There is abundant wildlife, including tigers, lions, and monkeys. Eight or ten elephants walking together is a normal sight in the mountains of Kerala. It is so beautiful and mysterious because of the way Nature intermingles with humans.

We are designed to respond to the visual and sensory stimuli of a beautiful environment. A tree, for example, has marmas, and it has feelings. Trees have senses and we enjoy their existence. When we are in healthy balance, we can see how connected we are with all living organisms.

This story illustrates that invisible connection. When I was about fifteen years old, my father was partially paralyzed and confined to bed for nine months. We tried all the treatments available to help him, but nothing worked.

The month before his death, we brought him back to our house. After a week, he showed an interest in walking and was able to go a short distance with support from others. One morning, when the natural world around us was very quiet, my father was trying to walk when suddenly he lost his strength and collapsed.

There was a huge papaya tree standing in the front yard. As children, we all used to climb on it. The papaya tree is like a coconut or palm tree; it is tall and very strong. As my father fell, the papaya tree also fell to the ground. There was no wind whatsoever and yet the papaya tree came crashing down. At the same time, there was an uproar from the domestic animals that were behind the house.

People who have knowledge of mysteries know that we can recognize what is going to happen by signs provided by Nature. The collapse of the papaya tree was a symbol for my father's death. All the men who were standing near the tree said of my father, "This is the last walk he is going to have, even the tree recognized it."

Indian Knowledge

From the ancient time, India has been very much connected to the outside world. There were universities in India four thousand years ago which provided the knowledge of everything that humans needed to know in order to flourish. People traveled from all over the world to study science, architecture, medicine, astrology, and spirituality in India. In Indian cities such as Malanda and Thakhasilla, people learned herbalism as well as the planning of houses, streets, and water drainage systems.

Through all its long history, India has known of the eternal existence of soul and spirit. The Indian culture recognizes that spirituality goes beyond variations of different religions, and thus it respects all religions. The Indian philosophy has the understanding that, when we die, the body will turn to dust and the soul will escape to find the next life. People there have known about astrology, the distance of the planets, and the particular influences of each one. The planets in the vastness of space may be empty of biological life, but they do emit a mysterious energy.

Our ancestors thought all these topics through very well, without a profit motive blurring their perceptions. There are so many valuable insights that have been lost to us because of money and control. The people who consciously assisted the evolution of the natural sciences had the pure intention of sharing this knowledge with everyone.

My efforts have been to coordinate the knowledge of Marma Science. I have created the herbal creams and teas so people could enjoy life, have self-confidence, and feel good about themselves. Bringing happiness into society brings harmony and joy into our lives. Everyone can feel secure. This was the pure intention of the great, ancient masters.

The scientific background which inspired my herbal formulas dates back to antiquity. For centuries, people have been trying, testing, and seeing the results of herbs and marma knowledge. The energy is subtle, yet we can see and feel the results. Many years of patience and curiosity brought me to this ultimate knowledge of beauty. It is important to understand natural truths and utilize them in our normal lives. Living in beauty means living in joy, happiness, and contentment.

How to Use This Book

Living in Beauty is organized into four parts. Part One explains Marma Science, what happens when the marma (energy) centers are blocked or out of balance, the interconnection of Marma Science and Ayur Vedic principles, and planetary influences. Part Two shows the reader how to care for the marmas through herbs and skincare, and the importance of digestion. In Part Three, the connection between outer beauty and inner beauty is revealed through discussions of spiritual practices, ending with a program for rejuvenation. Part Four is a treat for the palate and stomach, with healthy and delicious recipes for Indian food.

PART ONE

MARMA SCIENCE

~

CHAPTER ONE

Marma Science

Well-being is based on marma. Marma is the universal energy that connects humans, plants, trees, animals, and the earth itself in a nourishing life-support system of love, passion, kindness, creativity, and beauty. There is no translation for the word *marma* that defines its meaning completely. It can be compared to *OM* — the syllable which is said to be the sound from which everything in creation arises (according to the Indian Vedic sciences). We can say that OM has no meaning, but what we are really saying is that it transcends meaning.

Marma is an all-encompassing term for the very life force itself, as well as the pattern of channels through which it passes. It is God's energy that brings life to all creation. We live in a world that was designed in perfect harmony. Every part of creation has a part to play in the sacred symphony, and everything stays in tune as long as the current of vital force is flowing freely. The energy pulsation of the marma "song" is conducted as if by a grand synthesizer through the marma circuitry.

The actual shape of marma as an energy center is a triangle, which corresponds to the triad of body, mind, and spirit. The triangular, three-dimensional shape of the marma becomes a pyramid. Marma triangles are interconnected within each organism, and each organism is connected to the triangular pattern that extends throughout the universe. There is no distance in this chain of triangles because the energy travels so fast. The universe has no end — energy can be multiplied billions and trillions of times into infinity. Therefore, the entire universe is interlaced with the system of marmas.

Marma in the Human Body

In the Indian tradition, the generator of the life energy, or *shakti*, is known as the *kundalini*. The West is more familiar with the idea that everyone has an inner light. It is the same idea. This inner light is carried through the marma channels, which regulate the energy flow to all areas of the body and even outside the body. Outside the body, the light is known as the **glow**. Marma energy is electric in nature and comprises the electromagnetic field that is known as the human **aura**. Some people can see auras in detail. All of us can see that certain people seem to radiate vitality and inner security, as if a light were shining from inside them.

There are 840 million marmas in and around the body, all united through a structure of interconnecting triangles. Of these, **there are 107 main marmas that maintain the health of the body**. These marmas control the physical systems as well as the health of the mind and emotions. In turn, physical and mental well-being connect to spiritual experience when the marmas allow the inner light, or shakti, to travel through the chakras (major energy centers) to the top of the head. Body, mind, and spirit form the physical-mental-spiritual triangle of our being, which is governed by the marmas.

The constitution of the body can change when the marmas, any of the energy centers, are imbalanced. When the marmas are corrected, the constitution balances. Our breath, the heat in our bodies, our magnetism, our radiance, our light — all are based on the energy coming from the light centers of our body.

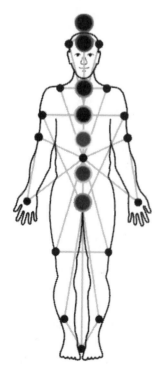

Triangular marma pattern

Marma Science is over 10,000 years old! Since ancient times in India, people have known about the 107 marmas in the body, including the seven main marmas, which are the chakras. They knew long ago about the stimulation of the marmas with various ritual applications of herbal paste on the face and body. The marma system is a concentration of electric current that can be compared to a circuitry of switches in the human body. When we unblock those switches, the light can be turned on. How do we unblock them? Through stimulation of the electromagnetic current.

Bioelectromagnetism

For many thousands of years, people have restored their health and well-being with herbal energetics and hands-on healing. However, for the last three hundred years, people have separated physics and metaphysics. We have been living with the false belief that the energy world does not exist unless it can be empirically demonstrated, yet few of us would go so far as to say that dreams do not exist because there is no film to rewind.

The phenomenon at work in rejuvenation is most closely described as bioelectromagnetism. Although Einstein and his successors have expanded the intellectual definition of physics, the reality of rejuvenation still remains on a natural, experiential level. Electromagnetism has different forms, such as gamma rays, light, microwaves, and radio waves. In the biological realm, light is a source of life and is the natural form of electromagnetism referred to in this book.

Prior to 1900, our biosphere was still relatively pristine. The most abundant form of electromagnetic energy on the planet was light, regulated by the solar and lunar cycles, with sudden lightning charges from ongoing thunderstorms. Small, innocuous amounts of radio waves, X-rays, and gamma rays came from space and radioactive minerals in rocks. Since then, we have adopted the use of more and more appliances, devices, and technological tools that have filled the atmosphere with artificial energies. This is all the more reason to protect ourselves with natural knowledge such as Marma Science.

As a force combining electricity and magnetism, electromagnetism accounts for the "charge" of different substances in the form of matter. The electric charge is positive/ negative and the magnetic charge is north/south. Opposite particles attract and like particles repel. This explains the interaction between atoms. The carrier particle of the electromagnetic force is the photon. The term "photosensitive" means that we have the capacity to react to radiant energy, especially light.

Matter can hold an electric charge and a moving charge can have a magnetic field. The human body has a strong electromagnetic field. We use this force for motors and equipment, so why not apply it to ourselves since the same laws are at work on a natural, subatomic level? With the proper skill, a gifted healer can transfer and conduct this energy into another person, strengthening the other's energy field.

That I am able to transmit this light is thanks to God, Who has given me the intuition to do this. Two of my teachers deserve most of the credit for my training. In my life, one of the most fortuitous aspects of my education was to learn Marma Science from a master who was not restricted by any particular beliefs. He believed that marma is all-encompassing – everything and everyone is included.

My other master in the sciences taught me the system of Yunnani medicine. Even though he much preferred seclusion, I am grateful to my master for his kindness in teaching me and his devotion to the tradition. Yunnani is a unique innovation of herbal medicine developed and practiced among the Kerala Muslims.

I also remember a great master from my childhood with thoughts of gratitude. I believe that mysterious old man transferred the gift of healing to me with his touch.

The Gift

My birthplace in my homeland is like a farm or ranch, with acres of land around it and nobody else nearby. Once, at about the age of eight, I was at home by myself when an old man with a white beard arrived. He had a remarkably strong build for an older man and an extra glow — very bright and powerful — all around his body.

This man came to my home and looked at me. His knowing gaze was totally charismatic. He talked about some of my physical problems in the knee and stomach areas. At that time, I had exactly the problems he described. He also accurately discussed the problems of my various family members. I was very thankful to him. Since I was home alone, I went inside to get a few pounds of rice as a gift for him. That is what my mother would usually do when visitors came.

When he took my gift, the vital old man looked at me and smiled. I will never forget the way he gazed at me. He seemed to be telling me that I could have millions of pounds of rice, whenever I wanted. Or perhaps he meant that what he was about to give me was worth millions and millions of pounds of rice.

He came near me, and I felt such a powerful energy that my whole body started to shake. It felt like I was covered with and surrounded by magnetic energy, and I was immobilized on the spot where I was standing. I was barefoot and I saw an energy coming up from my feet to my head. He came closer yet, and it was as though millions and millions of bubbles were traveling through my body up to my head. This all happened in a few seconds.

He smiled as he simply put his hand on the center of my head, at the crown chakra. I felt my whole body enveloped in a huge activation of energy and also experienced some very powerful feelings. He was still smiling at me. I remember he closed his eyes just for a second.

Afterwards, I almost forgot everything. When I looked up, I watched the man walking into the distance until he disappeared. I could not move from the spot where he had left me. I could not thank him.

His appearance was a mystery to me. He just came unexpectedly, and then he went away. There is no way that the people of the village could have avoided seeing the old man with the white beard, yet nobody in my village ever saw this unusual man.

When I asked my mother about my experience, she said, "Yes, there are people who learn *mantravadam* (the science of *mantras*), which gives them great abilities with the subtle energy body. Through their energies, they can recognize the proper recipient and pass their power and knowledge on to that other person. If you receive such a powerful blessing even once in your life, your energy will be awakened and you will have abnormal abilities. You will recognize people from past lives. You will have special connections. You will have healing abilities."

According to the mantric tradition, the wise old man — who gave me such a rare and precious blessing — and I are connected to each other through past lives, before and after death, and beyond time. Mantric tradition is still very common in Kerala. One can achieve strength and mental power through repeating the sacred sounds called mantras.

Beauty and Charisma

In the olden times in India, the technology of charismatic energy came from a pure comprehension of natural, vibrational healing. People learned that this early biotechnology had the potential for improving the quality of their lives, and making them into superior beings, by creating magnetic attraction. At that time it was a luxury to have the personal care of great masters. In modern times, it has become a necessity to protect ourselves with the wisdom of natural rejuvenation.

There is a charismatic kind of beauty associated with the personal magnetism of royalty. When such people walk into a room, all eyes are naturally attracted to them. The authority of confidence comes from deep within, from the complete internal balance of body, mind, and emotions. Life energy radiates from such people. In ancient India, the masters of the knowledge of life energy developed techniques to enliven the energy and create magnetic beauty. Kings and queens were willing to give up large tracts of their kingdoms to secure the masters' loyalty, thereby ensuring their own longevity and popularity.

This ancient science of beauty — based on the knowledge and use of secret herbal formulations that stimulate life energy — has now been revived for the first time in the modern world. Stimulation of the marmas draws out the internal glow, which can radiate through every aspect of appearance. By increasing the life energy, all elements of beauty can be integrated. The balancing and healing effects on all the systems within the body combine with increased mental clarity and energy to achieve higher goals and release creative impulses.

Releasing blockages caused by past traumas can mean the end of insecurity, depression, or substance abuse. In their place comes a natural routine of wholesome diet and revitalizing rest. The emotions are suffused with peace and inner calm, warmth and charm. People are spontaneously attracted to those who glow with health and beauty, making personal relationships more giving and rewarding, while intimate relations can bring complete satisfaction.

Wherever I go, I always look at people's energies, no matter what their color, gender, character, or history. We all are made of the same energy of God. Even with different cultures, beliefs, foods, and lifestyles, we are united in spirit. When we follow the laws of Marma Science, we are attracted to and enjoy the beautiful things in life.

Marma Science in South India

South India is the wellspring from which Marma Science flowed. South Indian people are aware of exactly where the marma points are on the earth. They are aware of exactly which way the marmas are affected by the location of their houses. With the same sensitivity, South Indians arrange trees and plant life in particular patterns in the areas surrounding their houses. One particular combination of trees is planted in the spot where they want a well. Trees such as coconut, cinnamon, and black pepper have the power to attract and absorb water from different parts of the earth. Planting that distinct combination of trees in the area where a well is dug means there will be an ample supply of water.

South Indians also situate herbal plants, particularly basil, in strategic locations around the house and in the corners of the house in order to prevent illness and other problems from developing. Basil is one of the best plants for the front of a traditional house; it protects the house from all kinds of insects and even disease. The same thing can be done with basil in this country, or with other herbs such as lavender and sage.

On the left side of the houses, Indians plant the jackfoot tree, which grows very large and spreads out extensively. Clove, cinnamon, black pepper, and other trees are arranged around the houses. Not only do the trees provide spices, they produce oxygen as well. Herbal plants also produce oxygen in the home atmosphere, so that people who live in that environment remain healthy. The architecture of the house itself is designed to circulate the oxygenated air to the inhabitants.

The Origins of Marma Science

Our connection with Nature is directly due to the universal presence of marmas and the universal energies that they govern. Human physiology and psychology depend on the functioning of the marmas — the energy channels that regulate every aspect of our body and, in turn, influence mental and spiritual states. When the marmas are unblocked and fully functioning, we experience a natural flow which is the connection with our environment — the life energy we share with all Nature. When the flow is maximum, we can achieve a state of true healing and subsequent wellness. Recognizing the laws of universal energy is part of the ongoing search for well-being. Obeying these natural laws makes it possible for miracles to occur.

Ayur Veda, the Science of Life, is one of the sources of knowledge about the marmas in India. Ayur Veda evolved gradually through the oral traditions and practical experience of generations until written records were set down. In the *Susruta Vagabada*, Charaka outlined the theoretical understanding of the marmas. This intellectual understanding became more sophisticated with a description of treatment for the marmas in the *Marma Shastra*, by Agasthya Muni, a renowned master from the Dravidian tradition. It is well-known that his knowledge of marma treatment came to Muni through his meditation in the forest of Kerala, at a place known as Agasthya Kuda Mountain in Trivandrum (which is now kept as a sanctuary). Trivandrum is respected as a cultural seat of learning and education; the healing tradition there dates back to the original Dravidian population. Agasthya Muni introduced Marma Science in Kerala and parts of Tamilnadu.

Ayur Veda brought into focus the balance of individual rhythms of people in relation to seasonal environments. The Vedic sciences as a whole are beautiful wisdom of the subtle energy body, symbolized by the Tree of Life. As bodies of knowledge, they are themselves alive and continue to grow with evolution.

DHANUR VEDA

In ancient times, when India was divided into thousands of small countries, there were thousands of kings. Each king developed his own fighting techniques, his own secret system of warfare. These systems were all originally part of the Dhanur Veda — the Science of Defense, or strength on the battlefield. The kings all studied techniques based on Dhanur Veda and were able to develop them to an unlimited degree. At that time, there were no war sciences that did not come from *Dhanur Veda.*

The ancient Dhanur Vedic techniques involve rigorous physical training, the achievement of strong willpower, and superior mental prowess. Dhanur Veda can be subdivided into many different components: a high level of technology, skill in mental development, extremely concentrated meditations, special diets in preparation for going into the fighting fields, and highly evolved martial arts. All these techniques were very highly developed. Many secret techniques of self-defense were extremely successful and kept secret for that very reason.

Since Dhanur Veda is based on the laws of universal energy, the results are extremely accurate and happen according to firm principles. The exact knowledge of how to harm another person by attacking specific, sensitive points of vulnerability on the body carries with it a great responsibility. Certain exercises can be practiced to develop and synchronize the hemispheres of the brain. From the practice of these exercises, extraordinary abilities may be developed. Superior development of the mind can give a warrior the ability to overpower any enemy — no matter how far away they are, no matter how strong they are.

The people who mastered these incredible, invincible techniques were able to defend or attack with powerful results in any war situation. One technique, called *Chundu Marma*, involved simply pointing at a person. By this simple gesture, the victim would fall down without even being touched. No matter how many enemies were in front of them, Dhanur Vedic warriors were able to control thousands of people by pointing their fingers and sending out energy. This feat was accomplished by controlling the entire energy which connects the earth and the human body through the universal marma system.

UNIQUE AMONG MODALITIES

Many people think at first that Marma Science is much the same as acupuncture, acupressure, shiatsu, and other modalities. But the concept of marma is really quite different. Of course, the energy centers on the body do not change. Rather, it is a question of how you work with the energy.

A true specialist in marma must develop his or her entire energy field to be able to generate and transfer pure and powerful life force. Working with other people to wake up their energy needs to be done with the utmost precision in terms of the functioning of the whole system. This is different from simply pressing on the points, causing energy to rush to particular areas.

Basically, improving the human body's quality of energy and amplifying the corresponding electromagnetic current, together with the knowledge of how to stimulate the interconnected layers of another person's body, is the ultimate power of marma. It is an energy transfusion. Everything must be done in exactly the correct manner in order for it to be effective. Then it is truly a profound transformation.

The powerful nature of Marma Science is the reason it has been one of the best kept secrets. For thousands of years, it has been taught in an oral tradition because of its extremely sophisticated nature. One becomes accomplished in it only after many years of dedicated practice. Marma is used in Kalaripayat as a powerful tool for stimulating marmas even from far away.

KALARIPAYAT *(Indian Martial Art)*

Of all the war sciences from Dhanur Veda, *Kalaripayat* has the most advanced fighting techniques. This martial art is a beautiful and sophisticated form of combat. The most potent methods of marma restoration were developed from Kalaripayat.

Many researchers have proven that the original techniques of Kalaripayat were passed along from India to other Asian countries. In my own study and research over the past twenty-five years, I have come to the same conclusion — of any of the martial arts is still practiced in its original form in India, in six different styles. The naturally exotic South Indian setting, replete with a variety of wild animals, provided the inspiration for this highly refined martial art.

Please see figures 4-10 at the center of this book
[Photos of Joseph Kurian performing Kalaripayat]

Graceful and fluid, with the finest precision of movement, Kalaripayat practitioners are poetry in motion. Some believe the martial art form of Kalaripayat contributed to the classical dance form known as *Kathakali*, particularly difficult in that it requires great flexibility and endurance. Both the martial art and the dance are popular in Kerala today.

The science of archery was the nucleus out of which originated numerous techniques using eighteen various weapons. Weapons used in Kalaripayat included the *otto kol*, a short curved stick; the *gada*, a weighty wooden mace; and *urumi*, a pliant sword belt that uncoils at lightning speed to seven feet in length. All these weapons are represented in the religious miniatures of Indian tradition.

By far the most powerful weapon in the arsenal of *Kalaripayat* was the knowledge of the vital marma centers of the body. In a reversal of polarity, this same knowledge has since become one of the deepest and most comprehensive healing arts, with a solid foundation in a very practical spirituality.

The Mahabharata

The story of Mahabharata, like Marma Science, is thousands of years old. The *Mahabharata* is some of the most profound literature ever written; it is the story of mankind.

Imagine a time when people developed such a high level of consciousness that they were able to directly perceive the laws of nature. They had no electron microscopes or particle accelerators; they literally saw the truth with their own intuition. This ability is called direct cognition.

From one generation to the next throughout the centuries, the knowledge of natural laws has been passed down in an oral tradition. Natural laws became the first literature when they were recorded on palm leaves by these ancient seers.

One of the most well-known stories from that time, the *Mahabharata* is an epic drama of human life. As such, it bears retelling and teaches us about ourselves.

The *Mahabharata* is one of the Vedic scriptures most important to India because it serves as a literary reflection of India's spiritual essence. This mythic epic describes the battle of human physiology and human psychology. On one level, it is the tale of warring families in society; on another, it is a spiritual conflict which our minds and bodies create within our individual souls. Once I delved deep and analyzed the basic concepts, I realized the human conflict described in the *Mahabharata* is exactly what I see when I work on my clients. The same fight, the same story.

After I had this insight, I realized that the *Mahabharata* is a reflection of human beings — mentally, physically, spiritually — projected as a story. As it so happened, I had the opportunity to work as choreography consultant and fight scene coordinator on the making of the movie by the same name, directed by Peter Brook. When we practiced with weapons which were the same as ones used in the ancient fighting arts, I realized we were stimulating the areas that hold blockages, the specific marmas in the body that could lead to healing.

In the *Mahabharata*, two families fight for the right to the kingdom. The Pandava family represents the good side, and the Kaurava family the bad side. The Pandava family includes five brothers and their one wife, Panchali. At the time of the story, the ancient game of chess had already been invented in India. The Pandava family lost a wager during a game of chess and was banished to the forest. They were supposed to disappear for fourteen years. If anyone found them during that time, the family would have to disappear again for another fourteen years.

After fourteen years of their secret life, the Pandava family fulfilled their promise of remaining undiscovered by anyone. During that time, they went through many difficulties, but were finally able to fight back the Kauravas and regain their kingdom.

When they had to vanish into the forest and jungle where humans would not set eyes on them, the Pandavas entered the deep forest of Kerala. During their exile, the Pandavas lived in a place called Munnar in the Panchali Hills (in the Kerala district of Idukki), where it has been said that the original footprints of the epic heroes still remain on the large granite slabs. Hundreds of years ago, this area was incredibly deep forest. To this day, what is left of the old jungle remains known as "Silent Valley" or "Valley of Silence."

Marma Science
The spiritual element is integral to the healing techniques.

The essential energy choreography of Dhanur Veda was transformed into the healing arts of Marma Science. If they are done without proper instruction and respect for the origins of the tradition, the effects will not be the same. Through thousands of years, each person has had to follow these rules and regulations very carefully to achieve the desired results. This is the reason why marma treatments are so effective.

Also, when a master passes this knowledge on to another person, he or she must be 100 percent certain that the person will continue the tradition. Masters know this intuitively. They look at the entire lives of potential students and are able to choose the right ones naturally. How can they know? Because of the Dhanur Vedic connection, which is a deep bond that goes beyond intellect. With persistence and years of practice, incredible power can be developed, such as expanding the capacity of the brain and sharpening the imagination and intuition. Life becomes easier and more creative.

There are many types of marma practice in India. In Ayur Veda, for example, there are some marma practices that are different from the Dhanur Vedic way of marma diagnosis, which depends more on the intuition and direct stimulation of the life energy. A master of the Indian martial arts is called a *Gurukkal*. After years of vigorous practice using the eighteen weapons and learning the most advanced techniques, a Gurukkal can do marma diagnosis very accurately. The incredible wisdom of the marmas can be used to read a person's energy field and perceive his or her condition in detail. If someone has an accident and falls down, or is attacked on some part of the body, that person will exhibit specific movements or illnesses by which marma specialists can determine what happened to them. This skill is acquired after years of regular practice. It is learned by practical experience. Such skill may require a long time for advanced marma.

Abstract intellectual theories do not easily take root in Dhanur Veda because it is the epitome of practicality. This requires patience and dedication, preparing the body and mind to be in absolutely perfect condition. The aura develops and becomes stronger. After that, a powerful, vital energy starts to wake up. People who have these abilities are able to recognize other people with the same abilities anywhere in the world. They can communicate with each other through this energy as if by satellite.

People from the ancient time used to talk about *Brahma,* which means absolute consciousness. Absolute consciousness is developed from marma stimulation. Dhanur Vedic marma practice empowers a person to see the new energy which is developing inside. This energy radiates like an incredible light that is impossible to describe. The sleeping light inside everyone can be awakened with the Science of Marma. Everyone can live in beauty.

CHAPTER TWO

Marma Damage
In Birth and Childhood

Marmas have a powerful influence on our whole being because they are finer than thought vibration, finer than emotional vibration. They provide the energy to maintain our bodies, minds, and spirits in healthy balance. It is only when the marmas become damaged that we lose the connection with our natural source.

At the time of our birth, we each have a destiny for this life. That destiny is associated with the planetary influences that exist at the time of birth. Although various disturbances can occur during birth, the blockages can be removed through the proper stimulation of the marma system and our relationship with destiny restored. Another way in which we are all connected is through the circuitry of stars we see in our galaxy. Our awareness of that connection is essential to our progress in this lifetime.

Our bodies are truly a gift for the experience of life. After death, the human body is just mud; it returns to the earth. The old body is worn out. Death is not something bad; in fact, it allows for our transformation. We are very resistant to and afraid of death, yet death is the most pleasurable transformation of our lives. If we could release this fear of death, then we could live better and enjoy life more. We do not want our spirit to come back to some dead thing. We want our spirit to enter a new body with a new birth.

Blockages from Birth

When there is trauma at birth, the marmas can be damaged. In olden times, the first seven days after birth were considered extremely important for marma healing. Any abnormality could be corrected by using specific healing techniques during the first week of life.

In the modern medical system, doctors have been taught that the mother needs rest, needs to be left alone after delivery. This is a major misunderstanding. Child and mother both need attention at this time. The child particularly needs the attention of its own mother.

In India, as soon as a child is born, we place it on the mother's chest even though she is tired. Have you ever seen happiness that brings relaxation into you? There is real happiness in that union — such happiness! After nine months of waiting and the pain involved in giving birth, there is such great joy. Joining the two in their relation as parent and newborn gives both mother and child a wonderful energy and makes them extremely relaxed so they both become content.

More than contentment, there is a physiological occurrence when the mother holds a newborn close to her heart. The functioning of the heart depends upon the proper electromagnetic current, proper energy, and proper aura. At birth, when the child is not strong enough to function alone, the child's aura is strengthened by that of the mother. Babies need some time to gain strength gradually from the heat of their mothers. Only a mother's warmth can give them that strength.

In humans, breath nourishes the mind and food nourishes the physical body. All three levels of mind, body, and spirit need sustenance. The child breathes and is given milk, but the added element of its mother's warmth is the only thing that can help the child to release the emotions and toxins that are inside at birth. The heat generated by the mother provides a newborn with the best foundation for childhood. It is the combination of mother's milk and mother's heat together which provides the happiness and health a child needs.

This process happens when a mother gives her baby a heartfelt hug, holding the baby to her chest. Basically, a minimum of three months is required for babies to have the very deep touch of their mothers. Absorbing the nurturing aura of the mother gives the child three ways of balancing: physiologically, mentally, and spiritually. Getting the care of the mother, the pulse of the mother, builds the foundation for a life of love and affection. Unfortunately, today, that first basic connection is missing for millions of children. Also, if the umbilical cord is detached before it has stopped pulsating, the supply of food from the mother's womb is cut off and the child is deprived of nourishment that is needed for the next three years.

The biggest loss to society may be the lost love and affection in the relationship between parents and children. This is why so many people have psychological problems. Quite fundamentally, the energy channels need to be stimulated, beginning at birth. The lack of suitable stimulation weakens the marmas and causes imbalances that result in all kinds of physical and psychological problems. Children often misbehave, and parents themselves do not have the psychological strength to see that their children are helpless and unable to recover their equilibrium. Part of the problem is that the parents themselves are already off balance under stressful conditions. These children often grow up insecure because they have missed the experience of a loving beginning outside the womb.

It has been my observation in working with clients in America that there are more birth blockages in this country than in any other. It is best for the mother to be with her child for a minimum of three years, providing the warmth and care that shape a secure young life. Ideally, a mother should breast-feed the baby for a minimum of one-and-a-half years. Unfortunately, the time is usually shorter and the mother herself is often not nourished properly after breast-feeding.

Self-Confidence and Trust in Others

Especially in the last three generations, people have come to experience a lack confidence in themselves and a lack of trust in others. Trust comes from confidence. We cannot be confident of ourselves when we have not had reassurance in infancy. Trust and confidence start at the time of birth when the child is taken from the mother's vagina and put on the mother's chest. The energy that comes from the mother stimulates marmas on the baby's chest, which start to stimulate energy all over the child's body. That is what bestows confidence and willpower from infancy, and willpower is what keeps a person alive in a state of well-being. All of this is the fundamental basis for a good life.

Sadly, this most basic knowledge of postnatal care seems to have been forgotten, and people think the mother and child should be kept separate. In reality, they are removing the child's ability to trust. This lack of trust is the reason people flounder and do not know what to do with their lives. They cannot focus on exactly where they want to go. They do not have that inner strength which was lost from the time of their birth.

Story of Childbirth in India

Let me tell you the story of the extraordinary care given to my sister when she had a baby. Labor started at 5:30 a.m. and finished around 11:00 in the morning. Once the baby was born, there were many preparations to be made for that week. Women were hired specifically to prepare special food for the mother: rice with herbs, very light fruit, pure meat from goats which were fed organically-grown food, chicken soup, mutton lamb soup, and other dishes. The animals were all raised on an organic farm so that the meat contained a very low level of toxins, which were removed before preparation.

The women mixed the meat with twenty-one different herbs to make a special type of food that needed no refrigeration. This food would keep for months without any problem, with only herbs used to preserve it. The women were basically making the entire substance into a molecular form that remained unspoiled for a long time. The food was specifically intended to help the new mother create abundant milk. Also, some of the herbs in the food acted to strengthen and firm her breasts.

When I saw that the women were giving her a little bit of alcohol to drink, I asked, "How can a woman who just had a child possibly drink alcohol?" I was told that a very small amount of alcohol is medicinal; it is stimulating. One of the women said, "The alcohol is being used to strengthen her stomach, shorten her intestine, and help her to circulate blood all over the body properly." This woman did not have a degree, but she was a well-respected midwife in the village. We considered her a doctor. She had gained credibility through her expertise in delivering babies into their new state of life as well as giving their mothers a new life.

That was certainly true in the case of my sister. In a couple of weeks, I saw that she had sparkling eyes and a beautiful body. She did not even look like she had had a baby. The baby was also doing very well, strong and healthy. He was crying with gusto; when I picked him up, he would push against me. Since he was drinking my sister's milk, he was naturally going to be a very healthy boy.

This maternal treatment continued for three months before and three months after the birth. I thought, "I should have been born as a woman. See what kind of care she is getting!" It was the most wonderful care I have ever seen. When she would move out of the room, there would be two people at her side to help her, to make sure she would not get hurt or hit the door. As the midwife said, "This is the time she has to be very careful. Any single hurt on her body can affect her marma centers." The midwife would cover different parts of my sister's body with towels: underneath the shoulder, between the elbow and shoulder, both hands and arms, both ankles and knees.

I asked, "What is the reason you are doing this?" She said, "Those places have to be protected even while she's sleeping. And they are not supposed to touch together during the night. The midwife also said that the towels were medicinal, too, soaked in herbs and placed in the sun to help with the stimulation of the energy.

When I began to study medicine and spirituality, I discovered that the priests in the temple used the same locations on the body as did the woman who cared for my sister twenty-three years earlier. The priests applied herbs and powders to the same areas, so I saw a similarity between the spiritual marma care of the priests and the more physical marma care of the new mother. They were really one and the same. The priests were supposed to keep their energy centers open so that, during prayer, the energy could circulate all over the body. Keeping the energy centers open created the electromagnetic current in their bodies and the aura around their bodies, so that when they blessed another person, they were transferring the effect of this energy.

In the same manner, the women had created incredible energy

in my sister. The midwife told me, "She will be like she is reborn. We are rebuilding her so she has a better chance. We are giving her a gift as she is giving a gift to the earth by having a child. It is a wonderful God-given opportunity after going through nine months of suffering to be returned to proper, beautiful health and be rebuilt herself." I have always noticed that my sister is absolutely attractive and is so healthy still. Even though she is close to fifty, she has a very powerful, strong body.

I remember it was very important to the caregiver that my sister watch where the child was sleeping. If the child was very far away from my sister's body, she would take him back and put him near my sister's body, telling her to always keep the infant near to her, even when he was sleeping soundly. My sister checked on her child often. She would make the time to do this because the midwife had suggested that it was an important aspect of motherhood. The midwife also asked my sister to take time during the day to put the baby on her chest and keep her arms around him — a sharing of the energy from mother to child so the heart would grow without any problem and the child would be more emotionally secure.

The Problems of Children

In the cases where I have seen healthy-looking children and mothers, the mothers had taken maternity leave for one year to have a child and did not immediately go back to their jobs. This gave them enough time for relaxation, which is why they looked perfectly healthy.

Unfortunately, I have seen many, many children — probably 60 percent of those in my practice — who suffer from very serious problems in their lives. They have a myriad of symptoms, including depression, allergies, and anemia. Avoiding illness is not possible for these children because they have already been damaged from birth. A child should have a natural resilience. However, that resilience is often compromised due to either traumatic birth conditions and/or inadequate nutrition.

At the time of delivery, many children have been wrongly disturbed or hurt, so they have acquired blockages in the neck area. The neck is the place where all the fibers of the nervous system join and spread out to the body. If anything happens to the neck, it can affect all the organs of the body. The way in which many children are delivered creates these marma blockages in the neck which adversely affect their lives. This has been happening generation after generation. A newborn baby born with marma blockages will exhibit unpleasant behavior. A child born without injury or malnutrition has no blockages. A healthy baby has a tender and nice disposition, making it easy to love.

All children are innocent. The real cause of their inability to adapt is the physiological blockages in the marmas that are connected to different parts of the body. These children can have a destructive mind set, an extreme weight problem, uncontrollable emotions — any number of symptoms. It is impossible for them to be balanced until the blockages are released.

In response to the problems of these children, society gives them psychological treatment. Here we have the crux of the dilemma. A psychological problem is a projection of their marma blockages as reflected in their character. Talking about the symptom does not by itself change the character of the person. Only the physical release of the blockage in the exact area where it occurred will eliminate the psychological problem. Once the marmas are repaired, the life energy is free to flow like a river. A healthy physical balance is restored. The organs of the body once again produce the appropriate hormones and other secretions which affect the emotional state. The thoughts and feelings are cleared as a reflection of the physical release. Since the cause is really very simple, the answer is also as simple as administering the herbal treatments necessary to remove the blockages.

We can also understand children better by providing calming, natural environments. The lack of relaxation alone causes tension that adds more obstruction to the system in addition to the original blockages. Relaxation and good herbal treatments enable the nervous system to become light, resulting in a dramatic shift for the better.

When I came to Europe and saw how children were kept in separate rooms and that mother and child were not even near each other, I thought of how much they were missing. So many of the nerve and marma centers in the children's bodies were blocked because they did not receive simple, natural nurturing.

When I did my consultations after that, I began to understand that it is not only physical love from the mother which is so necessary for the child's healthy development; the mother's words and expressions of love are important as well.

How much the children are losing when they do not have that wonderful hugging and heat from the mother! The mother's hug transfers the purest of heat energies to her child. I remembered the way the midwife had taught my sister to feed her child — the way my sister held him close to her chest and, after feeding, made sure that her body heat was stimulating the baby's heart. Then the milk he was drinking could be digested, and the digestive organs functioned properly.

In my Rejuvenation Program, pregnant women and their children both experience the benefits.

> As A. D. of New York said:
> Joseph told me the birth would be easy, but he didn't tell me how easy it would be. It only took forty-five minutes at home. The midwife didn't make it in time. It was just me and my husband. So much about beautification, but what about pregnancy and childbirth? I think it's necessary to see someone like Joseph. People run to doctors instead. My baby came out so clean and healthy and his skin tone was so beautiful.

And remember, no matter what happened to you at birth, it is still possible to recover your strength, whatever age you are now.

CHAPTER THREE

Marma Blockages in Adults

There is a saying that we are what we eat and what we think. Furthermore, we are what we were born with in terms of blockages to the body's energy pathways. The human body is like a huge building. One miscalculation in any part of the construction and the whole building will be offset. People are born with different blockages which manifest in different behaviors. The stressful influences in people's lives can cause even more blockages to appear. Accusing people and targeting them with dislike only makes them become more blocked.

Problems from Blocked Marmas

When marma blockages disrupt the flow of energy and nutrients throughout the body's systems, fatigue is a typical result. The effect of the blockages is compounded and toxins that should have been naturally eliminated become trapped inside, doing additional damage. When digestion is not working smoothly, for example, important marmas located in the face are affected, and facial features begin to show signs of aging. In addition, marmas regulate the replacement of cells. Skin cells are the soldiers at the defensive walls of the body; if these cells are not replaced in time, the old cells remain at their posts. Skin loses its natural resilience, and loose, wrinkled skin dominates one's appearance.

Blockages can also occur over time from small accidents and stress. Pressure at work or at home may build to the point where people feel "stressed out" and out of control. Their blockages have become too widespread for their bodies and minds to ignore.

I remember a father whose young son had developed a violent

temper. The boy was getting in trouble with authority, although he came from good family. Looking at the boy, I told the father that the boy had suffered an accident four years before that had injured his neck. An important marma had been damaged and this caused the change in emotion. Without treatment, the boy's temper would grow worse and most likely land him in jail. The father remembered that, four years prior, his son had injured his neck in a bobsled accident; his character had changed from that point on. The father enrolled his son in my Healing Program. A few weeks later, the father said, "My son and I were playing Frisbee on the beach today. All the love and harmony between us has been restored. I am so grateful. I have my son back."

The **marmas are also very susceptible to environmental influences** — the air we breathe, the food we eat, seasonal changes, and even the electromagnetic vibrations from planetary sources. This is especially true now that the ozone layer has been damaged. With our own protective auras weakened and the earth's protection depleted, these vibrations have very strong effects on the marmas.

In every country, the blockages differ based on aspects of the culture. From my consultations and observations in America, I can trace many blockages to child abuse. This condition seems to be more common here than in any other part of the world I have traveled. Also, the family is so broken up here that it cannot be depended on to help solve emotional challenges, which can cause blockages that affect the heart, spleen, and liver.

Excessive emotions coincide with weakness of the heart. There are more blue veins in people who are controlled by their emotions. As the marmas in the heart area become weaker and weaker, the functioning of the arteries and veins becomes slower. The purification of carbon dioxide from the veins becomes slower, so the carbon dioxide that is deposited in the veins causes varicose veins. How many varicose veins can we remove surgically without solving the problem? A weak heart causes some people's systems to fill with lymphatic fluid, which becomes toxic. In a woman, it can turn into cancer.

Skin problems can occur even though a person eats good food, yet someone who eats fatty foods may not develop skin problems. The former may be the type of character who is psychologically nervous, the result of blockages in certain areas of the body. When a psychological imbalance happens, a person can become emotional, anxious, and depressed. All of this has an effect on the endocrine system, which controls hormones, digestive organs, and bile from the gall bladder. When the gall bladder becomes disordered, it creates an overacidity in the stomach that spreads throughout the body. This acid can destroy bones and joints, causing arthritis and lumbago. So many illnesses all stem from the same problems.

Negative Stimulation

In my treatment experience, I have seen many people in different cities all over the world who are addicted to certain foods that make their glands react to negative stimulation. For example, certain combinations of foods such as sugar, caffeine, and wheat have a weakening effect on our adrenal glands. When the adrenal glands are stimulated with those food combinations, they produce excess acidity in the stomach, which becomes extremely poisonous. When we choose processed foods instead of nourishing the body with simple, natural foods, a vicious cycle of action and reaction begins. When our adrenal glands are already off balance and we see a violent scene on television, we become fearful. The stimulation of the reaction sets a pattern that makes us reach for the wrong foods again and again, so we become trapped in this cycle without even realizing it.

The addiction to negative stimulation also has to do with the combination of so many types of pollution affecting the natural electromagnetic current in the air, as well as the stress of modern society. All these unsettling influences can make us extremely fearful. Still, we need to survive, and so we continue with our blockages until, after a while, the blockages become part of our life. We only see the shadow that blocks the sun. We only think about negative things instead of positive because we are overcome by blockages. This endangers the positive energy as it struggles to assert itself in the face of mounting negativity. Again, we are unaware that we are negative and insecure because, after a while, that emotional state of being is so familiar that it is perceived as being normal.

Over time, memories become lodged in bone cells, brain cells, even skin cells, causing not only excitement in response to negativity, but violent resistance to positive things. Some people react like Dracula to the Cross when presented with my healing treatments. Instead of seeing a wonderful blessing, they feel threatened.

Keeping the Energy Channels Open

Through the practices and techniques of Marma Science, we can achieve a much better approach to various problems and an understanding of the solutions. Physical and mental ailments all start with blockage of energy channels in the body. Poisons begin to build up, causing poor skin tone, wrinkles, and blemishes. All the components of beautiful skin are controlled by the internal functioning of the body's systems that bring nourishment to and remove toxins from every skin cell. Once the problems are corrected internally at the marmas, the natural beauty of the skin is assured.

When the marmas are stimulated properly, energy returns. We can naturally regulate the amount of energy we need throughout the day for our activities. Our organs begin to function efficiently and the sense of vitality returns. Weight begins to return to normal. Skin, hair, eyes, teeth, nails, and all the other aspects of outward beauty begin to radiate health and attractiveness.

The key to physical and mental well being is keeping all energy channels open for the marmas, the energy centers, to conduct the transmission of vital life force. We cannot see these delicate marmas, we can only see their effects. We know they exist in the same way we know that electricity exists. We cannot see the electricity pass along a wire, but we see the light it produces when the current reaches the bulb. The analogy is appropriate since the marmas are the regulators of electromagnetic pulsations in the body.

This electromagnetic current is produced in the brain from the prana, or breath. When we breathe through the nose, the majority of the inhaled air goes to the lungs where it is processed, separating out the oxygen molecules and sending them through the bloodstream to all the cells. The remaining portion of the breath is processed in the nasal passages, where it is cleansed and transmitted directly into the cerebral cortex. Here, the cosmic, pranic energy found in the air is transformed into shakti, our individual life force.

The subtle energy pulsates through the *nadis*, which carry the electromagnetic impulses much like wires carry an electrical current. The pulses of the nadis are, in turn, controlled by the marmas. When these switches remain undamaged, the flow of pranic energy in the form of nadi pulsations is regulated efficiently so that every part of the body receives the nutrients and information at the proper time, and waste products of the systems are completely removed. When there is damage in the regulators, the flow becomes disrupted at some point. That disruption causes damage to subsequent points, compounding effects through the various systems of the physiology.

Sources of Marma Disruption

Marmas become damaged most immediately by trauma. Trauma is usually the result of accidental injury, either catastrophic or minor. If no marma healing takes place, trauma creates blockages at the marmas, both at the time of the impact and later as the body tries to repair itself. Other examples of trauma are surgery and the resetting of broken bones, which can radically alter or even eliminate specific marmas. Among the non-traumatic sources of disruption in the body's energy system are changes in the environment. If the system is subjected to conditions that put strain on a person's physiology or psychology, damage is inevitable. The stress of work, financial burdens, parenthood, physical over-exertion — all these will affect the functioning of the marmas.

In addition, chemical imbalance in digestion and disorders in the organs will result in marma damage. This is especially a danger of modern times due to the excessive use of chemical products in the processing of foods. Our desire for convenience and the potential for wide distribution of food products throughout the world economy have led to decisions about the handling of food that are disastrous from the point of view of the marmas. Blockages at one level can exacerbate those on another, as in the following example.

> D. P. of Long Beach, California, wrote:
> "You are experiencing negative mental states due to the imbalances in your stomach and intestines." These are the words you said to me in my initial consultation.

They keep coming back into my consciousness over and over and I am finally beginning to believe them. Actually, on one level I knew they were true the second you spoke them. It's just that my negative mental state prevents me from seeing or acting on the truth most of the time.

Just last Saturday I decided to enjoy some heavy food with my favorite football game. Not only did I have two pieces too many, but my team even lost. The next 36 hours were actually quite frightening. I felt tired and weak and yet could not really sleep. My heart rate would elevate and I would break out in a sweat. . . . My whole body felt acidic and spaced out. I am a recovering alcoholic and although I have not had a drink in over 17 years, I felt as though I was having a horrible hangover from an alcoholic binge. In time, my system rebalanced and I was able to function again. Although I will not eat heavy food again very soon, I still had a bowl of ice cream tonight and it's now 4:00 a.m. I am writing letters because once again I cannot sleep.

It seems I am still trying to drug myself, I'm just using different foods instead of drugs. I know the herbal treatments you have recommended for me would do a world of good, it's just that I'm not using them. My negative mental states are stronger than my need to get well.

Our modern way of life has created other environmental dangers which disrupt the earth's natural condition. The pollution of the air and water are obvious examples. The population increase, resulting in greater concentration in cities, leads us to compromise our bodies and minds dramatically just to have access to amenities and entertainment.

Planetary Influence
Another level of environmental influence comes from the electromagnetic vibrations of the planets, though the modern scientific attitude may make this difficult for many people to

accept. Consider that the pulsations of the nadis create a flow of electromagnetic energy throughout the body, regulated by the marmas. What would happen if the body were subjected to other electromagnetic energy from sources somewhere across the room? Could this other energy conceivably affect the ability of these regulators to perform effectively? And, if the interfering energy were coming from a very strong signal on some distant mountaintop, would that change the mechanics of the situation significantly? Moving the source of the influence to a greater distance, even into the heavens, does not diminish the effect.

Why does the effect exist? Because there is a correspondence between the microcosm of our separate individual existence and the macrocosm of the universe's existence. The body produces an electromagnetic current which carries information throughout the nervous system. Electromagnetic current is also produced throughout the universe, which carries information through the nervous system of the universe. This will be further discussed in Chapter Five.

When Marmas are Damaged

What happens when marmas are damaged? Marmas appear at the junction points of four main systems of the body and mind: the arterial, venous, lymphatic, and nervous systems. The **arteries** carry nourishment to all parts of the body. Therefore, in simplified terms, when the marmas are damaged, nourishment fails to reach all parts of the body effectively. These areas become weak and cannot defend against stresses and strains, including disease-carrying organisms that attack the body from the external environment. On the mental level, an equivalent weakening effect takes place, leaving the person without the mental clarity to think lucidly or the attention span to accomplish goals.

The system of **veins** removes toxins from the tissues and carries them to the organs responsible for purification and elimination. Therefore, when the vein marmas are damaged, toxins cannot get out and begin to accumulate within the body. Those that do make it to the elimination centers, such as the digestive tract, can get stuck there if blockages inhibit these organs. Unwanted chemicals taken in from processed foods and polluted air, excessive calcium from the manufacture of bone cells, and countless other poisons begin to build up. These accumulated poisons can create inflammation and tumors and potentially disrupt the functioning of organs and tissues anywhere in the body.

New cells are generated as old cells die and are carried away by the veins. If the old cells are not removed in a timely manner, new cells will not develop. In the case of bone cells, which are removed and passed out of the body through the nails, excessive calcification takes place if the veins cannot remove the unwanted bone matter. Calcification builds up in the junction marmas, breaking down their ability to regulate the pulsations of the nadis. This is the reason for black marks, rough skin, or even tiny amounts of calcium coming out of the skin. When the junctions of the vein marmas are blocked, some of this excess calcium can be pushed into the kidney, resulting in kidney stones. A client of mine experienced the release of calcium deposits after my Healing Program.

> L. M. of San Francisco writes:
> If I get any more energy, I'll be going to the moon. I feel so good and so energized. Joseph said the pains would go away in time. And most of it has — that was the pain in my hip and my lower back. It's fading, it's just simply fading. I get so much accomplished; I get so much done.
>
> My attitude is, "I'm peaceful." And I know it portrays — other people pick up on it. Little things don't bother me anymore. On my last session, I immediately lost five pounds overnight. I mean literally. I was able to get into my size 10 clothes that I had not been able to get into. When I started working with Joseph, the area around my stomach and waist started ballooning up and then the last time it was just poof! Good-bye! And it stayed that way. It was a real big impact and I'm still losing slowly. There are so many little things. Like the calcium deposits in my lower back. He broke it up and that was coming out through my skin in little tiny bumps and they're going away.
>
> My very, very first session, when he found all the

tremendous pain in my legs, he told me he added thirty years to my life in three treatments. I think he's added more years than that. I know he has. This year I turn sixty. I have more energy and feel better and healthier than when I was in my twenties.

T. S. of Cypress, California, had remarkable restoration of the calcium process:
Joseph's treatments opened the energy pathways so that my body could begin healing. My intestines had lost 60% of their ability to absorb nutrients. After the first program, my body began to change by leaps and bounds, throwing off toxic discharge. Small stone-like granules emerged from the surface of my skin on my face, neck, back, shoulders, and even my scalp. My body was throwing off calcifications and toxic substances that had been stored in my system for years. I also began throwing off a lot of mental toxic discharge. Painful thoughts and dreams surfaced that had been buried for years. Joseph knew of my past sufferings. I didn't have to explain it all to him. He looked at me and my heart area and said that he perceived the suffering I had endured. Joseph's treatments cleared up the blocked energy pathways in my body and helped my organs function normally and my mind to be free of suffering.

Many toxins are thrown off through the skin. The skin has been called the largest organ of the body. In recent years, the skin has increasingly been chosen by modern medicine as the vehicle to conduct substances into the body. When blockages impair this organ's ability to perform the functions of absorption and exfoliation, skin problems result. Old skin cells need to be exfoliated regularly, just as with the bone cells. When blockages prevent this, the skin cells are not replaced on time, new cells do not develop on time, and the skin begins to age. It loses both its ability to defend against environmental attack and its ability to throw off internal toxins.

The material necessary to build the physical body comes from food. After the initial digestive steps, the arteries connected to the intestines can carry off the nutrients while the veins begin to remove the impurities, or *ama*. When impurities reach the mind, toxification poisons the emotions, allowing insecurity, anxiety, and fear to dominate the psychology. People with such blockages can become very negative, even violent. This is one of the reasons why teenagers can be so difficult to cope with. During adolescence, the body changes rapidly, putting tremendous strain on the veins' ability to remove toxins. Toxification can become intense and shows up both physically in skin conditions and mentally in combative emotions.

There is also damage to the marmas governing the lymphatic and nervous systems that must be considered. These systems carry information necessary for the functioning of the organs, glands, and muscles. The information can be inaccurate or untimely, setting in motion a series of potential complications. Just as the arteries and veins nourish and cleanse the organs of the body, the lymphatic system informs and cleanses the nerves through the lymph fluid.

Controlling the temperature of the lymph fluid stabilizes the nervous system and brings balance to the mind. The entire information-processing role of the nervous system can become so damaged that the organs of perception do not receive information from the environment correctly. As a result, faulty information can be sent throughout the nervous system, resulting ultimately in actions that do not achieve their goals.

Presently, modern life is harder on the marmas than at any other time in history. However, the reversal of this downward spiral is no longer a mystery. Though our human body and mind seem infinitely complex, Nature has provided us with a relatively simple system to maintain it, with as few as 107 parts. If we can repair our marmas, we can rejuvenate our physiology, eliminate illness, redirect our psychology, enrich the emotions, and unlock our true spiritual nature. We can establish a new course for generations to come, ensuring a life of ever-increasing fulfillment.

D. P. of Long Beach, who was mentioned earlier, overcame his resistance. Once he started working with me, he felt progressively better as more blockages were released. He is maintaining a good physiological balance and writes:
My body is insisting that I write you a short note of

appreciation. After finishing my program this morning, I sat for a few minutes of meditation. For a few moments, my body experienced a sense of deep, deep relaxation and joy. This sense of complete peace and fulfillment within my body was so pronounced that my mind was drawn to it immediately.

My mind is accustomed to grasping and, of course, the experience dissipated as soon as I tried to capture it. I do not judge this. Everything that is happening to me is very positive.

My physical, mental and spiritual states have all undergone a complete transformation within the last ten days. I am uplifted in a way I cannot fully verbalize. I have been manic depressive in the past and have been quite "high" during my manic phases. My experience at this time is completely different from a manic episode. I feel quietly and calmly better, as though peace itself were slowly seeping into me . . . my heart is deeply appreciative and wants me to tell you so.

I look forward to each day now with a renewed sense of excitement and appreciation. My body thanks you, my mind thanks you and my spirit loves you. I look forward to working with you in the future and wish you and your work all the best.

Incipient Blockages
HEART

One of the most common problems all over the world is the health of the heart, the main part of the physical body. There are hundreds of reasons the heart may have problems. One reason is that the heart is regularly stimulated by the nerves. When we have stress, the supply of energy through the nerves gets blocked in the neck or shoulders area and does not reach the heart, so the message that sends stimulation or instructions on how to function correctly cannot pass from the brain to the heart.

The most common reason for heart problems that I have seen in my work is frustration — from our business, job, or even from our childhood. Frustrations can affect the marmas which correspond to the veins and result in blockage of the vein marmas. If people with heart problems press on their calves and ankles, they feel pain in that area from the excessive deposits of toxins which gather in the veins in the bottom of the legs. There can also be varicose veins or spider veins around the ankles. Also, modern medical doctors often prescribe antibiotics, which travel down to the legs and form deposits inside the veins of the lower calves.

When there is blockage, the energy has to be stimulated all over the body simultaneously. This is a simple concept I have observed in my clients, especially when we open up blockages corresponding to the spinal cord. Some people get extremely angry and express their fear, anxiety, and rage at the time of energy release in the third chakra. Keeping the energy circulating in a systemic fashion prevents a negative concentration in one area.

Another reason for heart problems is blockage of marmas in the large intestine and colon. The colon is directly connected to the heart. When too much blockage builds up in the colon, bacteria or viruses can spread into the heart. Many people try to clean the colon in this situation, but that is not the core solution. Many colon blockages are caused by blockage in the stomach marma, or even by blockage of some of the hand marmas that are connected to the colon. This has to be released in a perfectly balanced way, taking the whole system into consideration.

Cancer

Every disease has different reasons for developing. In Indian medicine, cancers are called *arbhutam*. Cancer exists in every culture in every country due to our emotions. The marmas are connected to our emotions. Depending on which organs of the body are reacting to our emotions, which part of the body is struggling with the emotions, or which marmas are blocked because of an emotional imbalance in our body, that area can be afflicted. If it is related to the bone marmas, it can make bone cancer. If it is related to the arteries and veins, it can make blood cancer.

My interest for a cure in this field grew because someone I

admired, who was a famous actor, developed a type of blood cancer which he hid for many years from his friends and the general public. He finally died after suffering tremendously. After that incident, I have tried to understand this disease. Unless it is in the later stages, the blockages can be released and the patient can go back to perfect health.

I associate breast cancer with an incident from my childhood. I used to play in the river with my sisters and my cousins. I did not know how to swim at the time I took a dive into deep water and almost drowned. Luckily, one of my sisters saw that I was drowning and she pulled me out of the water. The first thing I remember as I came back from the point of death was the touch of her breast. I always associated my escape with that touch of her breast. Many years later, I heard that my cousin was going to have surgery to remove her breast. My childhood connection between my escape from death and the loss of my cousin's breast was very meaningful for me psychologically.

I could not do anything for my cousin at the time, for I had no knowledge of how to correct it — even though I was an expert in many fields of healing. The experience led me to explore the nature of breast cancer. After years of study about how energy works in the body, I reached the point where I understood that most breast cancers begin with a chemical imbalance in the digestive organs, caused by the blockage of the nerve marmas. Another causal link is the marmas connected to the lymph system since nerve marma blockage will affect the lymph marmas. When any of these marmas get blocked, problems are created in the lymph glands or muscle tissues in the breast. There are also many other reasons for the cause of breast cancer.

The adrenal glands are part of the endocrine system. Pituitary gland, thyroid, digestive organs, reproductive organs . . . they are all connected to each other. Any weakness that develops in any part of the system can create a problem in a woman as a breast problem, in a man as a prostate gland problem. For a woman, it works on the upper part of the body; for a man, it works on the lower part.

Oversensitivity can also create a chemical imbalance. Chemical imbalance occurs from the imbalance of the liver and gall bladder. Gall bladder weakness creates a disorder in the bile flow when we get upset or angry. Overflow of the bile into the stomach will cause overproduction of acid in the stomach. In a woman, this acidity goes directly to the breast and to the eyes, hair, teeth, nose, tongue, ears, back of the head, and so forth. The concentration of the acidity in the breast creates imbalance in the calcium that builds muscle fibers, which can create cysts in the breast. The cysts can become bigger and turn out to be tumors which can be cancerous.

For a man, this happens with the prostate gland. The prostate gland is part of the endocrine system, and is also connected to the nervous system. All the nerves are concentrated under the occipital bone. Passage of energy through the heart from the back of the head will be blocked when men become emotional from frustration, anger, anxiety, or ambition. This could be caused by chemistry imbalance between couples, stress in people's professional lives, or the frustration associated with childhood when they wanted to express something but could not. The prostate gland is just a small part of the whole endocrine system, but it plays a very important role in the balance of that system because of the hormones and sexuality. Treating only the prostate gland is not enough to balance the whole endocrine system.

My curiosity brought me to discover many aspects of cancer that can occur in the human body. If a bone marma is blocked, can this be the cause of bone cancer? One of the most dangerous types of cancer that I have seen is blood cancer, caused by a build-up of toxins in the vein marmas. When I work on people with blood cancer, they become extremely emotional and much of the negativity they hold inside starts to come out. The same is true of people who have AIDS. Most of the people who have AIDS have a problem with the center part of the spinal cord where there is a very important marma which connects to every part of the body and directly affects the immune system. Any weakness that occurs in the central spinal cord creates a blockage of the solar plexus, where all immune disorders begin.

We sometimes make mistakes with diseases. We do not really think at a deeper level than the effects. For example, some years ago I heard that cellular telephones can create cancer. Does this make any sense? From my point of analysis, it is very different. I figured out that it is not the cellular phone causing the problem — it is because a person puts the cellular phone on the side of his head and bends the neck to one side to talk on the phone while driving, sitting, or walking. Emotions occur during these phone conversations which cause reactions in the digestive organs that change a person's chemical balance; toxins can build up in the veins. Depending on the position in which the person is holding his head and which marmas are affected by his thoughts and emotions, a blockage can develop anywhere in the body.

This is all based on my personal experience and observation, which may not be accredited by the modern system of medicine until evidence is gathered. Billions and billions of dollars have been spent just to see if there is some effect from herbs on the human body. For me, this is personal research — a culmination of experiences and observations from working with thousands of people over the years. My system is based on intuition and empiricism. There is a difference between laboratory experience and that of a personal healer with the direct blessing of God. This kind of technology has nothing to prove. If you want it, you receive it. Otherwise, you refuse it. The givers of this knowledge have nothing to prove. The only thing they want you to have is the happiness of your well-being.

Chronic Fatigue

Energy is most essential for humans. When our energy gets blocked, we get tired. We start to experience fatigue, sometimes called chronic fatigue. What is energy? Energy is like electricity. When the energy passes properly all over the body, or electric current is flowing in a building, the lights function properly.

That is the function of the electromagnetic current throughout the body. Each part of the body corresponds to different generators located in different parts of the body. Each generator has different functions. In the stress of daily life, any of them can get blocked and the corresponding area of the body does not function. We get fatigue syndrome in the cervical vertebrae area, some part of the brain, or any part where the energy is constricted or blocked entirely. Chronic fatigue syndrome is difficult to describe because it is based on the overall function of the right chemical balance in the body as well as positive thoughts. This is the nature of the chronic fatigue syndrome.

Impotence

Impotence happens in both men and women. Sometimes, impotence is confused with a lack of chemistry between partners. This lack of chemistry is itself a result of blockages in the marma system. For example, the initial attraction may suddenly begin to diminish as the result of day-to-day stress or a traumatic incident. Once blockages are removed, the chemistry quite often returns Partners become balanced again, which has a positive effect on mental, emotional, and even physical health. Love and affection improve our health. Much of impotence is not really from physical blockage; it has to do with chemical imbalance. In order to correct it, one has to regularly correct the blockage of the marmas. To a great extent, this will help impotence.

Other types of impotence can be caused by: excessive stress, nerve marma blockages, lymph marma blockages, lower chakra blockages, neck injury, or sinusitis associated with liver congestion. Weakness of the kidneys can result from too much pressure under the ears in an area called *manya marmas*. All of these blockages can be released with proper marma restoration.

Back problems

Back problems are common to every human being. Our lower back holds the highest concentration of energy, which is distributed to the brain and lower part of the body. Physical energy is produced from the stomach and heart. Mental energy is produced from the brain and navel. Mental and physical imbalance can create back problems because of weakness resulting from blockages of marmas associated with any of these major organs.

Most back problems are caused by the emotions and the liver toxins. For example, our emotions affect the acidic imbalance in the stomach. When we eat food, the food mixes with the acidic imbalance and gets distributed all over the body, including the lower back. This is one cause of back problems and back pain. Another is the build-up of toxins in the liver. Changing the seat you are sitting in most of the day can help limit the problem. The marmas in the back are all interconnected with the marmas that are connected to each of the above-mentioned organs and systems.

L. M. of San Francisco, California, opened up a new world with her treatments:

Before I met Joseph, my doctors considered my health to be very good. However, for the last ten or twelve years, I had had lower back pain and hip pain that was excruciating, and no one could do anything about alleviating that. My back hurt so bad that for almost, for a period of six months, I really couldn't do anything. The hip pain was so severe, that it would keep me awake at night.

I then met Joseph, and I heard that he had the ability to detect blockages within two minutes of meeting someone. I was so impressed. I knew, without a doubt, I had to meet him, that I would meet him and talk with him, and find out where the blockages were. I did have that opportunity and I was right. Within two minutes, Joseph was able to detect the blockages in my body.

What he found was that my problems were mostly in my bones, and what I really had to look forward to within the next five years could be hip replacements, or at the very least, cortisone injections. I then chose, without a doubt, due to Joseph's sincere knowledge, his sincerity and his knowledge, and his caring attitude, I chose to take his Healing Program. The very first one that I took, Joseph found a lot of pain in my legs that I didn't even know that I had. He told me that just by doing this first treatment, that he had added thirty years to my life.

B. G. of Aptos, California, explained:

To my surprise, Joseph just looked at me and I think held my hand. I think that there was some connection, when he told me that my problems had to do with a major blockage in the marmas in the cervical vertebrae. I thought that I knew that I had neck pain. I thought that was just chronic. I'd lived with it at that point over sixty years. I'm sixty-five now, so I was in my early sixties when I first came to Joseph.

So, that's what the major correction was — to open up the marma energy channels. So all this, the way that I looked, it's like fringe benefits. I didn't know outside of that, certainly I feel much better. My vitality's back. I didn't know that I was going to have such dramatic change. I guess I notice it most of all when I run into someone that I haven't seen for a number of years and they want to know what I'm doing. I mean I'll get comments from someone else who will say, "Oh, I'm getting older and you seem to be getting younger. What's going on?"

Ulcers and gastritis

Ulcers are the result of the overproduction of bile because of human *emotions,* overconsumption of alcohol, or ingestion of chemicals. Gas problems can be created by emotional frustration. Gastrointestinal disorders, it is quite well known, are emotionally connected to separation, loss of parents or children, death of a loved one, relationship difficulties. It is not so important as to what is causing the ulcers, but why we are not releasing the blockage. This must be done correctly.

Computer Use

I have found that computer users are affected in many ways from the more obvious carpal tunnel and vision problems to less apparent digestive sexual problems. According to my knowledge of the energy channels, I am aware of the problematic areas of the body where the energy typically becomes blocked.

Energy centers in the thighs are connected to the stomach, intestine, gall bladder, and liver. When these pathways become congested, the digestive organs are weakened, which adversely affects the eyes, ears, skin, and teeth.

More than fifty percent of the energy flow in these channels is directed to maintain vision and its related functions. Long, sedentary hours lead to excessive levels of carbon dioxide deposits in the veins, which also weaken the eyes.

More and more people find themselves facing a computer screen as a way of life. The effects can be seen in a variety of symptoms. These include weak eyes, back pain, weak wrists, indigestion, bad breath, white tongue, irritated lips, pimples, red veins on the nose, swollen nose, dullness, prostate gland problems, sexual weakness, and premature ejaculation, as well as a lack of natural spontaneity in social situations.

Carpal tunnel syndrome is a very common occurrence in computer users. This happens because of the chemical imbalance in the body's process of building the tissues and muscles. They are not strong enough to hold the eight pieces of bones that move in the wrist. Every time they move, it hurts the nerves and that is what causes pain and inflammation.

The combination of creams and teas in Marma Skincare is a sophisticated system of herbal energetics that is especially beneficial for computer users. A simple, self-care routine that takes only minutes a day, this program will clear out the blockages that have built up in the energy channels, releasing the current of life force to flow along the body's circuitry. People notice that symptoms are alleviated, eyesight is stronger, digestion improves, and temperament is more calm and relaxed.

> T. S. of San Francisco, California works hard as an executive:
> I had the good fortune to meet Joseph Kurian about a year ago. I had separated from a company in the Silicon Valley, where I'd had a very high-powered, high-pressured job, that required me to travel a lot. I left my employment due to job burnout, and feeling that my creative energies were gone.
>
> I took some time off to refocus my life. During that time, a friend introduced me to Joseph, and I was lucky that I was receptive and open to new ways of approaching my life, and realigning my life and my values to be more in synch. Through several hands-on treatments with Joseph over a number of months, I regained my energy and my enthusiasm for life, figured out what I wanted to do professionally, still within the high tech industry, but with a more centered approach to my life, enjoy my work, feel renewed and rejuvenated, and have also

eliminated all health problems that I had experienced as a result of stress and my life being out of balance.

I also have enjoyed the benefits of Joseph's skincare products, which I've found have made a major difference in my skin in terms of how it feels and looks. I think the products really affect the quality of one's skin, in addition to moisturizing the skin surface. You feel it from the inside, as well as how it looks from the outside. A number of friends and family have commented on how I look much more vibrant and healthy than I did a year ago. Everybody can benefit from Joseph's products and treatments. They help one to regain a sense of balance and be their personal best.

Abuse

Sexual abuse or any kind of abuse has negative effects on the physical, mental, and spiritual bodies. Mostly, they affect the lower intestinal area or the navel area where the nervous system conjoins. Frequently, there are also permanent menstrual disorders. Colon problems can be a part of these blockagages. Properly releasing the blockages there permits the problems to be resolved. It is not that easy because this happened with most people in their childhood, but it can be done. Psychological help is a must while releasing the blockages.

V. N. of New York, New York, expresses her story of abuse and recovery:

As a child, I had suffered from the tyranny and sexual abuse of an alcoholic father. This awakening to sex included shame, guilt, pain, and helplessness, which affected me all during my childhood, adolescence, and adult life. During my adult years I developed menstrual problems, digestive problems, sever hip and lower back pains, migraines and mood swings. I had poor sleep and frequent nightmares. My neck, back, and shoulders were hard as rocks from hypertension. I overcame many obstacles and behavior problems through my religious faith and various self-development habits. I maintained an active life. I forged ahead as a high achiever.

Ironically, I never seemed to be truly getting ahead. I could not find myself, and my body developed physical problems over the years. Additionally, most of my relationship with men ended in confusion, pain, and bitterness, with deep feelings of abandonment.

My early years of self-help treatment included hypnosis, spiritual growth through religion, therapists, exercise, and hobbies, but none of these ever brought me to a point of sustainable happiness. These forms of help were brief. Also, no modern medicine or medications could help my rapidly deteriorating body. Everything offered was basically nothing more than a superficial remedy. No matter how bravely I forged ahead and no matter how rational I was in understanding the events and issues that had occurred in my life, I still felt out of place and had bouts of depression. I never seemed to gain the joy of life I wanted.

I met a really great man whom I married. In spite of our excellent marriage and trust, I still could not find a deep happiness and inner security. My physical body became fragile and weak. I suffered bouts of depression and bad moods and had poor sleep. I'm not the type to expect my husband to be responsible for my own problems and I never dumped my past problems on him. I believed in letting the past rest and only in moving forward. However, I could not quite reach a sustainable point of joy in my life. I always thought happiness had to be worked for and that it was something only some people were born with.

I found out about Joseph's program from a health paper. I went to him because of my physical ailments. Joseph's program was different than anything else out there. I had immediate results from the very first self-care herb and oil program. I began to release physical and mental pain I had buried deep in my body. I continued with this program and moved on to do the Healing Programs. My body and my mind began an incredible healing journey I never expected possible.

One of the hardest things for a sexually abused woman to do is trust. I had built up so many defensive blocks and mental escape loops that I didn't know life without them. I thought it was just part of being a thinking, rational human being. But Joseph's treatments released the pain from me layer by layer. The more I trusted him, the more results I gained. I could feel all the defensive blocks I had built up over the years leave my being as Joseph worked on my body. He pulled negative energy out of me and I could feel and experience the release in my body, mind, emotions, and down into my soul. More toxins and negative discharges occurred during the weeks following the treatments. The detoxification process for me was quite dramatic as he removed years of anger, pain, resentment, sorrow, confusion, bitterness, and suffering that I had held in my consciousness and body for years. Calmness, and peace of mind moved into my consciousness for the first time in my life. All the defensive loops and psychological barriers were melted away. I found an inner strength I had never experienced before.

Joseph was patient, kind, and very sensitive through the whole healing process. Each healing session brought my mind to a new level of awareness and helped me to understand issues at different levels of the detoxification process. It is as though something woke up in my brain and I gained an instant understanding of the whole picture. There was no rationalization or philosophy to think through. My mind clearly understood the nature and cause of the illness in my life. One of the best things about my healing was that I came to understand the root causes of my suffering as I released them. Joseph's Healing Program was a genuine answer to my prayers. Immediately after my treatments, I saw a noticeable improvement in how men treated me. I mean, I was no longer getting a predatory gaze from certain men. I was ignored by and basically invisible to those types and treated with kindness and respect by others. Also, I sensed that men were now looking at me, in my eyes (as a whole person) instead of just at my body parts.

My physical body is also healed. I do not have any back or hip pain or digestive problems and my migraines are completely gone. Emotional stability, happiness, and joy have moved into my life. I no longer ever get depressed or suffer moods, even before my period. I lost all the weight I wanted to (without trying) and there is a wonderful sense of energy moving through my body where it once was blocked. All the tightness in my shoulders, hips, stomach, and neck are gone. My sleep is deep and restful.

After the treatments, a new calm awareness and spiritual maturity came into my being which was gentle and serene. For the first time in my life, I have a kind of happiness and zest that never leaves me. I no longer have the mental fears and phobias I had before. For the first time in my life, I feel a deep and a profound sense of security. I look years younger than I did before the program, and I have a healthy radiance to me. The deep lines in my forehead disappeared and my skin became clear, soft, and supple. Beyond the physical level, I noticed that I felt different about myself. When I look in the mirror, I like who I am looking at. Not just my face, but my whole body. I smile more - almost all the time. I have a positive self-esteem and sense of full womanhood and self-identity I never had experienced before. My friends are drawn to my sunny radiance. I get compliments from men and women both and feel a genuine contact with them. My husband also appreciates the changes in me. We were always very close, but the treatments have brought us closer in many ways which I never expected or knew could ever happen. I look and feel beautiful inside and out for the first time in my life.

I cannot say enough about Joseph's unique healing abilities. His ability to locate the blockages and clear them from the body, mind, and emotional systems is extraordinary. Joseph's Healing Program is the real thing. Each healing session takes me to a higher level of perfect health and happiness. And the effects of the healing have been permanent. I am writing this in hopes to reach other women who have had sexual abuse and suffered - to let them know there not only is hope, but a true and permanent healing that can take place in their lives. Joseph's Healing program is the most remarkable experience I have ever had and I am very grateful to him for his gift of healing in my life.

The Ultimate Stimulation is Love

Imagine that you are climbing a mountain. You are using all of your strength and concentration to hold on to the cord that you are using to climb. This is an analogy of love in real life. If anything happens to that cord, we are finished. We become totally out of balance. The focus we have on the cord is our stimulation that gives us confidence. That confidence can encourage us to reach whatever goals we want to achieve.

Many people have held tighty to that cord, but it has been broken so many times that they no longer trust the rope. Usually, people who have been betrayed will project what happened to them on to others. It can be someone else's name, appearance, energy type, or astrological similarity that they recognize. The other person is completely innocent. This happens because of the blockages. Hurt feelings affect the pulse and the area four fingers above the navel, which is a vital area where feelings are recorded. As long as the blockage is not cleared out from there, it can be repeated or recreated in other circumstances.

Insecurity can manifest in many different ways in the human mind and body. It is a weakness of the heart chakra and also of the first chakra. Insecurity can affect the reproductive organs as well as the heart chakra. This disease is more dangerous than any other because it can create disease in other people. In a sense it is contagious by causing problems in others when it is projected.

These projections can also be abstract idealism. Some of the people I have seen in my client base have been frantically attached to certain beliefs without understanding the science of various disciplines to connect to God. Every religious discipline has its own science. Every one of them in one way or another are connected to each other like a freeway system. Everybody has the intention of going to the same place, but everybody's taking different routes. Because someone else is taking a different route than ourselves, it does not mean they do not reach their destination.

People try to protect their God even though God has the most strength of all. This protection is unnecessary. Rather, the release of insecurities in ourselves is paramount so that *we* feel secure and protected. For example, the most ironic behavior a person exhibits is to bring all their medicine for me. In the middle stages of their release, they bring a lot of names of other healers and tell me how important it is for me to know them. The middle stage is the time when all their insecurities come out. Usually, at that time, I get a lot of gifts of different medicines, vitamins, and everything to make sure that I will be healthy. It is a living truth we can see among everyone, how protective we are when we become weak or get blocked. People do the same thing with their beliefs. Some call it fanaticism. Some call it insecurity.

We become afraid, so we end up wandering into the unknown. A typical result is misguided spirituality. Many people end up with wrong beliefs or become fanatical about their beliefs being the ultimate strength. We do not want to risk losing the illusion.

Physiologically, how does this breaking of the rope affect our system? Our spirit is the endocrine system that consists of the pituitary gland, thyroid, thymus, digestive organs, and reproductive organs. Any imbalance that happens to the pituitary glands affects the hormone production. If the hormones are not produced in a regular cycle it can imbalance the menstrual cycle in women and cause emotional imbalance in men. Both will experience effects in the digestive organs.

The digestive organs consist of adrenal gland, spleen, pancreas, gall bladder, liver, kidneys, and intestine. Any imbalance in the gall bladder is the result of bile disorder that creates gastrointestinal problems. Once we have a GI tract disorder, whatever food we eat does not digest properly.

Constant GI tract disorder also weakens the sensory ability of the intestine. Normally, our intestine analyzes the digested food and sends messages to the brain. The brain gives orders to carry the food to make the cells. As a result of GI disorders, we can gain weight within a day or two, become depressed, or develop any number of symptoms.

You may have noticed that people who have been separated or suffered unexpected tragedies suddenly look unhealthy within twenty-one days. One needs to take care of the imbalance in the body as soon as possible. Otherwise, the toxins are released into the liver and penetrate every layer of the body three times.

When someone is in love, their focus will stimulate the pituitary gland. Spiritual devotion stimulates the thyroid. Affection is the emotion which stimulates the thymus. Self-confidence gives the relaxation to keep the digestive organs healthy. Attraction is a combination of these qualities that helps a person to be sexual and charismatic. Awakening these qualities makes a person balanced. There are many barriers to achieving this kind of balance. A lack of chemistry between partners is common. Sometimes the love becomes possessive because of insecurity. This is all because of the blockages in a person.

After witnessing many examples, I tried to understand what the solution could be. While searching, I realized that the answer for this is already in the rejuvenation I developed from the Kaya Kalpa treatment — a person can reach ultimate happiness and have perfectly balanced mind/body/spirit. After applying this knowledge, I have seen people's careers improve dramatically. Their businesses become more successful. People who have been alone for a long time find their partners. And many, many more wonderful achievements.

The overall most important thing is that the human life on this earth is very small when we calculate the distance of the planets and stars, the timing of life and death of a planet or solar system. Our lifetime is not even more than seven seconds by comparison. All this competition we build inside ourselves can be put into perspective. Instead, our precious seven seconds can be a thoroughly enjoyable moment in time.

C H A P T E R   F O U R

Marma and Tridosha

To comprehend the universality of marma, it is essential to understand the interrelatedness of all things. In the divine holographic design, the life force current of marma is pulsating throughout the cosmos. Marma is our world and ourselves.

Marmas and Chakras

The universal energy enters through the portals of the chakras into the human body. **The chakras, or *mahamarmas*, regulate the spirit and are the energy source for the marmas.** The marmas are spread throughout the seven layers of the body in a triangular pattern.

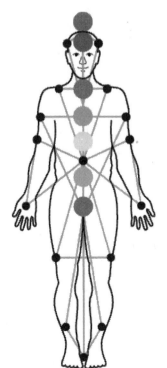

An individual marma is in the shape of a triangle; the circuitry of marmas in the body is in triangular formation; the universal marma system extends in an infinite triangular pattern. Thus, the marmas of a person are the communication mechanism that unites the individual with the cosmos in the journey from and back to Light. There is a system of laws of universal energy wherein an ideal frequency exists for each aspect of creation. When there is a free, uninterrupted rhythm of vital force, harmony reigns and the splendor of life is gratifying. Even one broken triangle offsets the universal balance.

To use an electrical analogy, the chakras act as transformers to convert the energy from a primary circuit — universal marma — to a secondary circuit, the marma centers. The marmas act as transducers, actuated by pranic power, and supply the energy in another form, the *doshas*.

The rejuvenation I developed holds the knowledge of clearing the energy pathways of blockages and keeping them open for the flow of current. This is accomplished by the resonance of herbal energetics and personal treatment. The key to this understanding is the unlocking of life energy held within the nervous system. The potential life energy waits in the base of the spine. When freed, it moves through its own energy channels upwards to the top of the head. Along its path is found each of the seven chakras.

Please see figure 11 at the center of this book
[Location of chakras on the body]

THE SEVEN CHAKRAS

Muladhara chakra (base of spine) governs the sense of security and physical comfort associated with basic biological needs. When the energy of the Muladhara chakra is unlocked, attending to these basic needs becomes effortless.

Svadhishthana chakra (genital region) controls procreation and the desire for family, including sexual desire. The freeing of this energy brings sexual potency and satisfaction and promotes harmonious, loving relationships.

Manipura chakra (navel) gives rise to the desire for wealth, fame, power, longevity, and all the manifestations of success in the outer world. Until this center is fully awakened, the drive for material success can never bring contentment.

Anahata chakra (heart) is the pivot between material and spiritual experience. When aroused, it increases devotion, compassion, love, and selflessness. Now a person is no longer bound by the desires of body and ego.

Vishuddha chakra (throat) awakens the desire for deep knowledge of life, the ability to discriminate the truth from non-truth.

Ajna chakra (third eye) awakens the desire for enlightenment, the desire to transcend even the most subtle forms of relative existence.

Sahasara chakra (the crown) opens the thousand-petaled lotus. With that, one ascends beyond desire altogether, and individual consciousness opens to supreme Self-realization and enlightenment.

Vedic Understanding of the Human Body

To comprehend the existence of the marmas we must first understand the components of the human body. According to Vedic medical science, including Dhanur Veda and Ayur Veda, there are several levels to understand. Consider the body at its basic level as principles governing how matter manifests. All matter is created out of the Five Great Elements. These are known as *Pancha Mahabhutam* in Sanskrit, but in ancient times these five elements were acknowledged among all cultures.

THE FIVE GREAT ELEMENTS

Akasha (ether) is the field of existence which supports the manifestation of matter. It represents the principles governing space and distance that create the separateness of objects.

Vayu (air) represents the principles governing the gaseous state of matter.

Tejas (fire) represents the principles which transform matter from one state to the next gaseous or other state of matter.

Apas (water) represents the principles governing the liquid state of matter.

Prithivi (earth) represents the principles governing the solid state of matter.

Based on these principles, formless cosmic spirit is transformed into individual material forms. All the properties of the multitude of objects in the material world are created out of the intricate interactions of the five great elements. The transformation is a continuous interplay between timeless principle and material creation. It is the eternal dynamic dance of *Purusha*, the unchanging Father principle, and *Prakriti*, the creative Mother principle.

Like all creation, our individual reality is governed by these principles. We are continuously being formed out of the five great elements. From cosmic spirit, our own individual creation unfolds as mind, sense organs, organs of action, and the doshas all coalesce. Manifesting from pure principle into the field of individual matter, the composition of the five great elements determines not only the physical body, but all aspects of individuality — body, mind, intellect, emotions, even personality and character.

THE MANIFESTATION OF THE FIVE GREAT ELEMENTS

Ether is associated with desires and needs, sexuality, fear, anger, and sadness.

Air manifests in all aspects of movement, such as walking, sitting, running, and stretching.

Fire manifests in hunger and thirst, sleepiness, laziness, and mental clarity.

Water manifests in all the fluids, including sperm, sweat, saliva, urine, and the fluid of the eyes.

Earth manifests as the structural elements of the body, such as bone, flesh, nerves, skin, and hair.

As components of the external world, the five great elements are perceived and assimilated in the form of energy by the five sense organs of the human body — eyes, ears, nose, tongue and skin.

The image of the body as a temple helps to describe the importance the marmas play in our physical, mental, and emotional health. God has provided all the materials necessary to construct our temple and the technology for us to keep it in perfect repair. With this technology, the temple can be maintained as a place of profound spirituality at all times. In this temple, we can achieve pure knowledge of ourselves as manifestations of cosmic spirit. In fact, our direct connection with the source of creation is contained right within our bodies in the form of the marmas. The kingdom of heaven is quite literally within us.

Marmas and Doshas

The marmas exist at the junction of the unmanifest and the manifest, finer than the material out of which our bodies are constructed, finer than the cellular level, the molecular level, or the atomic level.

The symbol of the triangle is again represented in the *tridosha: vata, pitta, kapha*. Difficult to describe, the **tridosha is the balance of energy forces** that coordinate and organize physiological and biochemical activities, translating the external to the internal. More meaningful is the correlation with their respective elements — vata as air, pitta as fire, and kapha as water. The doshas create a physical reflection of these principles within us, ideally stabilized in delicate balance for physical, mental, and emotional well-being.

Vata dosha— Air, principle of movement.	Governs all bodily processes in which movement is necessary, as in the nervous system.	Nervous system — 72,000 nerves which converge at the navel marma — controlled by the brain, which produces electricity.
Pitta dosha— Fire, principle of conversion.	Governs all bodily processes where heat is necessary, as in endocrine system.	Endocrine system — pituitary gland, thyroid, thymus, digestive and reproductive organs.
Kapha dosha— Water, the Earth principle of solidification.	Governs all bodily processes where cooling is necessary, as in the vascular system.	Vascular system — heart, arteries that move the blood throughout body, and veins that purify and channel the blood back to the heart.

In simplified terms, food is digested by pitta, broken down by heat. Kapha controls the fire of digestion and allows its extract to be conveyed through the water of the body. Vata moves the nourishment through both the heating and cooling phases and allows the transport of the extract of this digestive process.

Ancient medical science maintains that it is from four elements — air, fire, water, earth — supported by the field of existence itself, ether or *akasha*, that all matter is constructed, including our own body and mind. We can understand this in physical terms when we consider that every cell in our bodies reproduces itself within the span of a month or so, and the sum of that process is a completely new body.

A constitutional predominance of certain doshas is set at birth. A healthy individual is able to maintain a balance among the tridosha, which influences the whole system. The three systems need to be operating as a triad of dynamic equilibrium in the transposition of energy and matter. There are multiple processes of assimilation and elimination going on in the context of environmental fluctuations.

Since cellular creation is governed by the relative balance of the five elements, reflected in the relative balance of the three doshas, when the doshas lose their balance the resulting body will have problems. All aspects of our individuality can be affected — body, mind, intellect, emotions, personality, and character.

The system that regulates the flow of information and energy through the three doshas is the system of marmas. This explains why the marmas are so powerful and why, if unblocked, they are so effective in the healing process. Conversely, if there is blockage in the marmas, imbalance occurs in the tridosha. Every marma is related to these tridosha forces in the body.

Depending on the location of the blockages, the corresponding imbalance in the doshas will bring about problems in that area of the body. By removing blockages in the marmas, we have the potential to maintain our body, mind, and spirit exactly as Nature intended. Our balance depends on our connection with our natural source.

Story of Tridosha Imbalance

The experience of one of my clients demonstrates the results of an imbalance of the doshas. He was only thirty-five years old, yet all his hair had turned gray. He had problems with his teeth, eyes, nose, and every part of his body. He was so weak, he could hardly eat anything. He had all kinds of allergies. While trying to decide about taking my herbs, he asked, "Do you have this herb in it? Then I cannot have it. Do you have this in it?" He would not believe that the combination of herbs creates a synergy that is distinct. He was bringing up such a list of things, but he really believed that he was enlightened and that he was perfectly right.

He had been sitting and meditating for years without any proper exercise or proper cleansing. His cleansing was accomplished by drinking gallons of water. Of course, that was one of the biggest mistakes he could make. Every time he drank too much water, he would totally upset the chemical balance of his stomach. Bile coming into the stomach in order to digest food would get diluted, so whatever foods he ate did not get absorbed into his body but went right out through his colon. The undigested food was not assimilated or digested, and he had become weaker and weaker.

His skin was extremely hot. His body was so hot that he thought it was the kundalini rising up. Plus, he looked extremely sick, even though he believed he was becoming spiritually enlightened because of the heat. He had read in some book that when the kundalini wakes up, there is a certain amount of heat that occurs in the human body. Unfortunately, his heat and kundalini heat were miles apart. The heat he experienced was a result of his whole marma system becoming disrupted and therefore increasing the temperature.

The body has to be balanced with vata, pitta, kapha. It should not feel too much heat or too much cold. Ideally, this man should have felt a moderate temperature. Circulation has to work properly for the three systems to be in dynamic harmony. When this man's tridosha became imbalanced, his heat level increased and he became extremely nervous. As his heat level increased, it created a chemical imbalance within him. The chemical imbalance meant that his adrenal glands started to malfunction, his digestive organs (adrenal gland, spleen, kidney, pancreas, liver, gall bladder) developed disorders, and his acidity level increased. The whole body became unwell. That is what was happening to this poor man. He had peptic ulcers in his colon and stomach. His esophagus was very weak because acidity came up into the esophagus and burned it.

When I was near him, I could feel how badly he needed pure energy. People who are sick try to draw healthy energy from others. The current which the healer has is as essential as food. That is why many healers look weak or sick, and their bodies get weaker as they lose more energy. Basically, sick people are totally missing that free-flowing energy current, so naturally their bodies are trying to attract it.

Healthy people have a strong aura and conscientiously increase their electromagnetic current frequently. The truth of Marma Science teaches that inside of us we have an electric current, or electromagnetic field. The electricity produced through proper breathing doubles the aura, which is the electromagnetic current. All that is needed is to circulate the aura in every part of the body; if it is directed to only one side of the body, it is still not enough.

Releasing blockage of the marmas is the key to circulating the auric energy. When the aura starts to develop, it takes ninety days to strengthen it and three months to three years before the aura is able to freely and completely circulate energy. It depends on the blockages. It takes three years of regular cleansing to remove blockages in the liver. The liver needs to be pure in order to function as a filter, eliminating toxins. Once the liver is healthy, a person immediately starts to feel a difference.

It is important to emphasize that by "cleansing" I am not referring to the many intestinal cleanses available in health food stores. Overly aggressive cleansing of the intestine, colon, or liver can weaken these organs and detract from their ability to distinguish between vital and non-vital elements. There is a systematic way of finding out where the blockages are in the body and releasing them properly. This is the cleansing that is done in my energy readings and personal programs.

In the most fundamental teachings of ancient Dhanur Veda, tridosha is compared to the actual body, mind, and spirit, which correspond, respectively, with the vascular system, the nervous system, and the endocrine system. The body, being the vascular system, becomes the kapha of Ayur Veda, carrying the water which is the blood flowing through the circulatory system. The mind, being the nervous system, becomes the vata of Ayur Veda, bringing the air or electricity which is traveling through the nervous system. The spirit, being the endocrine system, becomes the pitta of Ayur Veda, providing the fire that heats the digestive process.

Seven Marma Layers

The seven layers of the body build the material construction of the body according to the way in which the individual doshas reflect the principles of the five great elements.

Please see figures 12-19 in the center of this book
[Seven layers of the body]

The Seven Marma Layers

Arterial marma refers to the vessels carrying rich red blood to deliver oxygen and nutrients; vascular system essential in building healthy new cells.

Venous marma refers to the vessels carrying blood from the capillaries to the heart; vascular system of cleansing to remove old cells and toxins.

Nerve tissue marma refers to the network of filaments conducting the activity of the nervous system; it allows the pranic energy to pass through every part of the body and creates the electrochemical balance.

Lymph and plasma marma refers to the fluids of the body which carry food to all the organs, tissues, and bodily systems; nourishing liquid that also bathes the cells; lymph system balances body temperature and supports the nervous system.

Flesh marma refers to the muscle fibers, ligaments, tendons, and fat; it protects and insulates internal organs and tissues while it maintains the body's strength and ability to move.

Joint marma refers to the areas wherever bones come in contact; it provides flexibility of movement and expression.

Bone and marrow marma refers to the bone structure which supports the weight of the body; also the soft matter within the bone structures, including the marrow, spinal cord, and the brain itself. Together, they provide the framework of the body and the structure for consciousness.

Clearing the marmas balances the doshas and opens the channels of nourishment and information to the seven layers of the body. As nourishment passes through the body, each of these layers extracts the food for its own uses and then prepares the conditions for its consumption by the next layer in the series. Each layer organizes different functions of the body and then, in turn, gives rise to the normal functioning of the next layer.

In a healthy body, each layer supports and nourishes the next. Therefore, each layer must be functioning properly or the subsequent levels will be adversely affected. If the marmas are out of balance, that imbalance will carry through to the seven layers and the material body will be constructed with inherent weaknesses. When marma blockages weaken one layer, successive layers fail to get the energy and information they need and weaken in turn.

The five organs are the next level of this materialization of the body and maintain the functioning of the seven layers. Imbalance in the three doshas inhibits the work of the seven layers and thus creates dysfunction in the five organs. The tridosha also regulates the five great elements in the body, which are represented by the five organs:

> *Ether* corresponds to the brain,
> *Air* corresponds to the lungs,
> *Fire* corresponds to the intestines,
> *Water* corresponds to the kidneys,
> *Earth* corresponds to the heart.

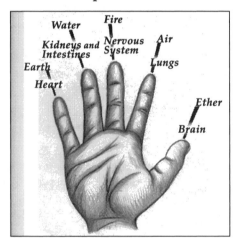

Marma and Prana

As complex as this becomes, there is still the mental component of the body to consider. In Marma Science, humans have two stomachs, one for the body and another for the mind. The digestive system for the mind involves the sinuses and the brain. If we compare ourselves to a factory, the buildings and the machinery must be powered by electric current, carried through wires from a generator. The brain is our generator. The nervous system and lymphatic system are the wiring of the body.

The energy that is transformed by the generator into the electrical current is called prana (breath). Eighty percent of the prana that enters through the nose goes to the lungs and is then distributed through the body along with the extract of the digestive process.

Twenty percent of the prana is purified in the sinuses — the stomach of the mind — and goes to the brain as subtle energy. The cervical cortex transforms this energy into electromagnetic impulses.

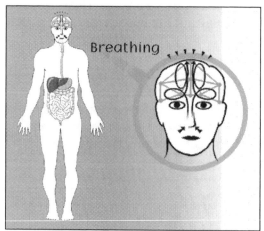

Stomach of the mind

The impulses that have been transformed from prana into electromagnetic current are conveyed by the nadis. The 3.5 million nerves act as insulation in this process, maintaining the flow of the current to every area of the body. Of these, 72,000 are the main conductors, the major branches of the system. And, of these, there are 700 that support the rest. In turn, 350 of the 700 are most critical to the uninterrupted flow of current within the system.

The complexity of the integrated functioning of these systems — arteries, veins, nerves, lymph vessels — is a challenge to our comprehension. But as intricate as these systems appear, a pattern has been given to us. For **at the junctions of all these interdependent systems can be found the regulators — the mysterious 107 marmas — which govern all the complex activities and interactions**. The regulators control the pulsation of the nadis. The task of the marmas is to make certain that information and nutrients get to the right places at the right times, while toxins are removed to the right places at the right times. When the energy regulators become blocked, the three doshas lose their balance and the five great elements do not manifest in the natural way. In turn, the seven layers do not perform their functions correctly, and the five organs of the body are constructed with weaknesses and deficiencies.

The key is balancing the marmas. Everything in the functioning of the entire body is dependent on the efficiency of these regulators. And since the body is being reconstructed at every moment, these regulators have the potential to assure proper functioning of body and mind, as long as any damage to them can be repaired in time.

"Alternative" Medicine

There are solutions for everything with the science of Nature. Research in a lab does not always coincide with the laws of Nature and the universe. Conclusions are based on cells that are replaced in a matter of five or six days, and response can be influenced by the tests themselves. Traditional medicines that have been time-tested for thousands of years are not the same as the medicines born in a laboratory during the last few hundred years, which are more appropriately called "alternative medicine." In fact, these "alternative" methods are often derived from the ancient recipes of the Indian sciences. The recipes are analyzed and the chemical contents which are inside the herbs are made into synthetic medicines because those herbs are not readily available, being grown only in tropical countries.

What I am offering is the oldest of the old and the best of the natural, the best of the knowledge. Where is it coming from? Traditional medicine means the ancient recipes; when they are altered by chemical analysis to find the chemical substances, it is altered medicine, not traditional. Nobody derives herbal formulas from chemicals; the chemicals are coming from the herbals.

These altered medicines do have effects. One day when I had the flu, I took 24-hour relief tablets from a supermarket. It helped me to control the cold within a day. Seven years ago, I broke my ankle and, even though I am expert in fixing broken bones in any part of the body, I went to an alternative hospital. They were able to help me. So it is possible to integrate the alternative medicine into our lives within limits, along with these ancient, traditional medicines which have soul directly from universal energy.

CHAPTER FIVE

Marmas and the Planets

The Marma Science I am telling you about in this book was known to Indian scientists many thousands of years ago. They knew that the structures of the stars — the shape of triangles in the stars, the shape of squares in the stars — are the same as the structures found in our human bodies. All the marmas are very much connected to the stars. Our bodies are built with the same harmonious patterns and are energetically connected to the stars and planets. Throughout our lives, we receive energy from the light produced by the heavenly bodies.

Each person has a unique pattern of planetary influences, dependent on the time and place of his or her birth. A picture of the sky at the moment of birth, from the place of birth, would show the most prominent influences in the heavens. Each human is connected to a chain of stars that forms the pattern which is present when he or she enters this world.

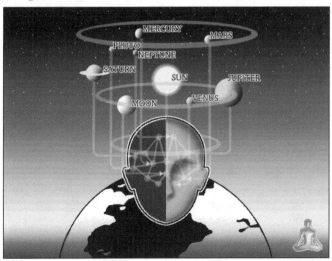

When we look at the universe, we see how small this planet is. There are billions of stars, many of which can have planets. How big are they really? According to scientific understanding, our planet is small and the distance to other planets is small. What blocks us from each other? What creates complexes? What makes us distance ourselves from each other and the world? Billions of stars are influencing our energies. They are interested in giving us the best energy. Unfortunately, we are blocked from receiving the best energy from them. Let us try to receive that energy by opening ourselves up.

In ancient times, Indian scientists knew how important it was not to have any energy blockage, or interference in the flow of vital life force, at the time of birth. They would immediately release any blockages that occurred so the infant could connect with those stars which would provide the light necessary to wake up his or her aura. When a child was born, calculations determined what vibrational influences were in effect at the exact time of birth. From that, the potential damage to the marmas was calculated. From the marma damage, predictions were made about the child's potential physical and mental health as he or she progressed in life. Corrective measures were taken so that the negative influences would not have any effect in the future. In other words, the child's destiny could be changed for the good.

The universality of marma energy is a profound reality. Since marma is the power supply for the cosmos, it is the common denominator for everything that has vitality. We can observe similarities in our own energy patterns and those of the planets.

Mother Earth, our home planet, is finally being granted more of the respect that is owed to a life form that sustains other life. The earth has its own nervous system and is made up of the five elements — ether, air, fire, water, and earth — as is everything in the universe. In the Vedic vocabulary of physics, every body of matter is connected to all other matter by these five elements or principles. And so, just as we have marma junction points regulating our human system, the earth has its marma junction points regulating its systems, and we are directly connected to them.

South Indian Architecture

The cosmology of the stars profoundly influenced traditional Indian architecture. South India is the most knowledgeable place about Marma Science. Everything there is created according to this science, with the knowledge of exactly where the marma points are on the earth and exactly which way the marmas are affected by the way we situate and build cities, temples, and houses.

In the South Indian culture of *Dravada*, cities and temples were built according to scientific calculation, using Marma Science to encompass the energy patterns of the heavens, earth, and human beings, with methods of channeling the life force in a strong, smooth flow. The different sciences combined the laws of energy for astrology, geography, and human well-being. These laws evolved into a blueprint for planning everything well; Nature provided the breathtaking backdrop. Scientists calculated the position of structures in locations aligned with a positive energy flow. This placement coordinated and concentrated spirit into one space. In South India, the architecture of the temples has a distinctive beauty, unlike any others in India. In South India one can also see this imposing pattern of construction in the surrounding areas. For example, Madurai is a city in South India built according to the shape of the *mandala*, which is the most mysterious and fundamental of the Hindu symbols.

Earth Marmas

The universe contains millions of planets, each one contributing to the symphony of the whole. Each planet emits both good and bad energy. Like the auras which emanate from our bodies, planetary auras can be either positive or negative, depending on how well the planet is being cared for. Planet Earth has marmas, as do plants and animals, which form patterns on the earth. The earth's marmas have a vibratory pattern which is affected by every other planet's electromagnetic influence. The human body's marmas are affected by the earth and the forces affecting the earth. In this same way, planetary influences are continuously affecting the human body.

Sometimes people travel in different parts of the world and

sense their connection to a particular area. Even though it is their first visit to a certain place, they have a feeling of familiarity. They recognize the pattern of energy from a past life.

In its natural state, there are seven layers of atmosphere that filter and purify planetary lights, protecting the earth. This has become more critical in recent years as Earth's armor — the ozone layer — has become depleted, allowing the vibrational influences of other heavenly bodies through in stronger doses. The ozone layer above the earth has been destroyed to such an extent that the damaged area is equal to the size of one-third the planet! Consequently, both positive and negative energies from the planets are penetrating us more intensely than ever before.

When imbalance occurs in the human body, there is disease and death. Likewise, planets can also get diseased and die from the same kind of pollution. Waste destroys the planet and spreads out to the universe. There is a pattern in the universal system that can be thrown out of balance in a chain reaction. When the earth's marmas are congested, the chemicals produced from the earth are increased by planetary influences.

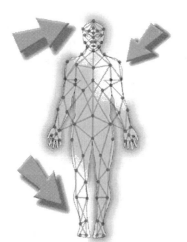 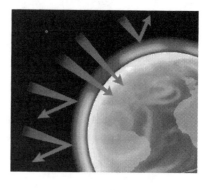

Aura Missing on Human Body and Earth

Chemical factories, smog, pollution, and the waste from the past two hundred million years pollutes our air. The waste we are putting into the air is what is destroying the ozone, which is the skin around the earth like the skin around our bodies. When that skin is broken, waste from outer planets comes through to our planet.

As long as the skin of Earth is not protected properly, we are vulnerable to interplanetary wastes in addition to our own. Such pollution creates disease and weakness in different parts of the body, inviting viruses and bacteria to enter, just as when the skin on the external part of the body breaks, bacteria can come inside much more easily.

The Parallel Bodies of Earth and Humans

Consider the parallel of our physiological bodies with the body of planet Earth. We have fever, colds, sneezing, allergies. Sometimes we have circulatory problems; other times we suffer from constipation or diarrhea. These same problems can occur on the planet Earth. Phenomena such as geysers, volcanoes, weather patterns like El Niño and La Niña, and hurricanes are examples of existing and recurring imbalances. Most of these are routine cleansing impulses of the earth. However, when these forces become exaggerated, it is a symptom of suffering in the earth's marma system.

Insofar as the heavenly influences are not properly filtered, they come through and directly affect some part of the earth. Planetary light, or magnetic energy, acts upon specific marmas on the bodies of people living in the affected areas of Earth. During certain times of year, some countries have periodic episodes of uncontrollable disease. They do not know why — it just sweeps through. The sudden impact of the unfiltered energy affects the energy patterns of our body, where the marmas are blocked immediately. People who are living in that location instantly develop a weakness and any virus, bacterium, or amoebae can enter the body.

Ordinarily, prevention of bacteria is a natural process of the energy patterns of the body that stimulate the marmas. If there is already blockage in their bodies, this planetary effect will have a greater influence on people in that part of the earth more than the rest of the world. It doesn't go everywhere — it goes to one particular part of the world and immediately affects that entire area on the body of the earth. But even though it is concentrated on one section of the earth, the virus doesn't attack everyone. Why? Some of these people manage to keep their bodies healthy and their marmas stimulated. Their marmas are very strong, so it has no effect on them.

I saw a movie a few years ago about a huge viral epidemic in Africa. The movie was fictional, but it was based on reality. Scientists were doing research there and found that the people who contracted the virus were all dying, with one exception — a healthy priest who seemed to be the only one who was immune. Every day the priest was burning a certain herb as part of a spiritual ritual he was doing. The herb was penetrating his body and stimulating his marmas, so the virus had no effect on him. The ancient herbal practices have tremendous powers of purification and protection. Herbal rituals have a powerful effect on the marmas. They have the power to stimulate our own energy so that we can be immediately protected from the planetary effects on our marmas.

Planet Earth and human beings are created from and function with exactly the same five great elements. There are three doshas in balance in the earth just as we have three doshas in our body — vata, pitta, kapha. On Earth, air, fire, and water are the wind, the light, and the rain. We say that the flat surfaces of Earth are the air dosha, the mountains are the fire dosha, and the oceans are the water dosha. The five elements are represented by the five organs of Earth in the same way that the five elements are represented by five organs in our human body — the brain, lungs, intestines, kidneys, and heart. The five elements are all controlled by triangular patterns of energy which are really all coming from one unit — the marma. What makes the correspondence between microcosm and macrocosm, between human and planets, so significant for Marma Science is that ancient seers cognized the influences from planetary sources. God has given us this paradise on earth. We could be enjoying it in a very positive way rather than contributing to its destruction.

Kali Yuga

Since we have entered the time of *Kali Yuga*, a destructive mentality has awakened in humans. Negativity has more place than the positive. False gods appear. This is a clouded time when truth is difficult to see, when distractions keep us from following natural, healthful ways. We may prefer television to friendship, anger to love, chemical to natural foods, and we may resist or be unable to see change for the positive. People naturally get confused and fearful. El Niño has produced many changes in the earth, including earthquakes, weather pattern disruptions, and unusual, dangerous winds. There are predictions for a great many incidents that are going to happen in the future.

In order to counteract this situation and save our world, it is time for the ancient, natural methods of protection and rejuvenation to be revisited. Physiological blockages create not only illnesses, but also destructive minds and mentalities in people. I have seen people who have such a high level of destructive blockage in their marmas that they could easily turn on their own parents. This tendency toward destruction is not necessarily their own fault, but can be ascribed to the characteristics of marma blockage.

Racism, as a good example, is based on 100% insecurity. I have seen people who were racist with very negative behavior. They become different human beings once their blockages are released. They become totally loving toward everyone.

Unfortunately, racism and insecurity could increase more and more in the coming years because of the environmental changes. To the degree that our immune system is compromised because of malnutrition and pollution, illness can easily be created. This creates more insecurity in a person. When that happens, people will look for new gods, new beliefs, and become more nationalist and separatist. Everyone wants to be identified and become part of something when they cannot feel their own strength.

In order to change this situation, moral education has to be expanded to more than just reading new literature. For the coming centuries, if we do not make preparations in advance, humans can experience very painful consequences. The education system needs to teach respect for life.

One day one of my clients who is a teacher came to have my treatment. That specific day, she was very tired. I asked her, "What happened?" She said, "This was the most exhausting day. Today is the day I am finishing my class. All the children were blaming me for all the bad things that I have done to them.

This is one of the saddest days of this year and my life."

Is that the education we really want to promote? Can we call this a system of education? Teachers should be getting prizes and gifts as thanks for the struggle of teaching them for one year. I asked her, "Not one student said thank you?" She said, "Yes, one boy sent an e-mail to thank me so the other students would not know."

I still remember when my teacher took me in his lap, put the rice on the floor, took my finger, and helped me to write on that rice. My first word. I still remember the pulse coming from his heart to my heart. That pulse gave me the strength of being able to learn anything.

That kind of connection should be established between teacher and students. There is where the moral education starts – as a strength from the teacher.

To overcome the blindness of the Kali Yuga period requires effort. If we don't make that effort, however, the spiral will continue to accelerate downward. This is why it is of the utmost importance that everyone awakens this universal energy and connects to each other in a positive manner. Kali Yuga does have a silver lining — any positive effort made with pure intention will receive God's full support.

Since the age of fourteen, I have known that Marma Science can correct the imbalances in the universal energy. Each person can awaken the energy from inside the seven chakras, pushing out the electromagnetic current through the seven layers to the outer part of the body. This amplified energy field around the human body acts as protection from any influence coming from outer planets, as well as that coming from the environmental happenings on planet Earth. When intuition develops as part of this process, we start to see things as clearly as crystal. If, all together, we can wake up the universal energy and connect to each other, people's fears will disappear and the world will be a beautiful paradise again.

PART TWO

CARE OF THE MARMAS
The Way to Beauty

~

Chapter Six

Physical Health

Beauty starts with health — physical health, spiritual well-being, and their interconnection. Beauty is synchronized on all three levels of body, mind, and spirit. If any level is unclear, then nothing is in balance. In order to attain complete beauty, all three levels need to be in balance — a balance that begins with health.

A Priest's Herbal Ritual

When I was studying the mantravadam (very powerful techniques to achieve the energy for outside powers), I learned of rituals in churches and temples that used certain herbs to catch spirits or remove them from humans. In fact, a Catholic priest in India uses the same methods, although in a different way. One day I went to visit a priest near my province, who was known to be a devil-catching priest. Almost 150 people visit him every day. It is like a daily festival going on there. When I went, hundreds of people were waiting to see him. There were very strange noises — women crying and speaking with men's voices, people speaking perfectly in languages they had never heard before. This all happened while they were in the session.

I was sitting outside the office where there was a big bore well with a wall. It was quite comfortable. As I was watching the show, a man about 25 years old came near me and started looking at the cross at the end of the chain I was wearing. After that, he also started to look into the well. He asked, "Why are you here?" I said, "Just to see the show." He started to talk so badly about the priest that I had a feeling there was something wrong with him.

After some time, I saw three well-built men come to take this man to the priest. He threw all three of them at once, as if he had the strength of an elephant. Finally, many people together got him inside the office of the priest. The priest asked, "Who are you?" The man answered with a name which was not his own. "I am someone who died three weeks ago. I came to take my friend away with me." Then he said the name of his friend and people agreed that the friend knew someone who died a few weeks ago and was buried at the municipal cemetery. Finally, the man swore at the priest, "I will leave him!" He screamed in a very loud voice and became unconscious.

Later, I became friends with this priest and we discussed the medical and spiritual aspects of this phenomena. His experience was very intriguing. He really believed there are outside influences that can affect humans. After assisting him for a while, I learned a lot about this subject. Indian Christianity is very advanced in terms of spiritual healing, with a close connection to many aspects of Indian culture.

Historically, it was very common to see miracles. What is called "phenomenal Christianity" existed in Kerala 1600 hundred years ago. In my family, there are many priests and nuns. Most of them are rectors (one rector has 1000 students). In fact, my cousin wrote a compilation of old and new versions of the entire bible. It is considered one of the largest, most comprehensive bibles in the world and he has been rewarded by the Pope in Rome.

After assisting the priest for a while, I realized that what he was doing was not very different from what I was studying at the time with my teacher of mantravadam, even though my master had refined the methods from the original practice. After the priest had released the man's problems, he recommended herbs and sacred incense. He helped me to understand more about the ancient way of rituals and herbals they used as medicine in his practice, which is not much different from those of my mantric teacher. But the discussion with him helped me to open to the possibility of creating this program fifteen years later with herbals adapted to the creation of oils. When a client follows any of my programs, I recommend the beneficial use of the same oils.

What the Face Shows Us

Every single aspect of God's nature is contained in the healing technology of Marma Science, coming from the twelve thousand year-old Indian philosophy. On the physical side, the balancing of disorders is fairly simple: correct the marmas and the difficulties recede as the system becomes balanced. On the spiritual side, it is the vital force of the subtle energy body that forms the template for the physical body and connects the individual nimbus, or aura, with the universal energy system.

What is charisma? Charisma is actually the electromagnetic current of the Spirit — the aura that we develop within ourselves and that emanates around us. There are 840 million marma points or locations arranged throughout the body in a triangular pattern, extending beyond the body about four inches. The aura contains the energy that surges through all these marmas.

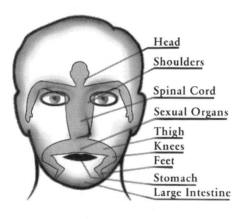

Head
Shoulders
Spinal Cord
Sexual Organs
Thigh
Knees
Feet
Stomach
Large Intestine

Every single organ of the body is represented on the face. There are twenty-five major energy channels connected to the energy centers on the head, reflecting internal health on the surface of the skin. Anything happening on the face will give us a clue as to the condition of the corresponding organs.

BAGS UNDER THE EYES

Each area of the body is connected to other parts. I have seen people who have tried everything to remove the dark circles from underneath their eyes. In most cases, the discoloration and puffiness is connected to blockages of the liver and kidneys.

The liver is the purification factory of the human body, where toxins can concentrate when we sit in one place for a long time. Consequently, the toxins from the liver come up and get stored underneath the eyes, causing the darkness. Sitting for a long time also causes the kidneys to get blocked, which creates water retention in the body and the heart is forced to work harder. The water is taken to whichever area of the body can discard it. When the water cannot be discarded, it is taken to those areas and stored. The first storage area is underneath the eyes because it is the place where the water is most easily discarded or stored.

Sometimes bags beneath the eyes are a reaction from the digestive organs, connected to the liver and kidneys. For example, drinking too much alcohol, taking an overdose of medication, or eating too much heavy fruit during the day may create puffiness under the eyes the next morning. Taking a light diet will help to cleanse the liver, especially along with the Marma Teas. One of my herbal products, Renewing Eye Cream, erases the effects of the day before; people have also noticed remarkable changes after a Marma Facial Massage.

In today's society, it is all too common to have the bags surgically removed and the area around the eyes tightened instead of controlling the diet and taking care of the liver and kidneys. When the skin is tightened through surgery, what will happen the next time there is excess water or slow functioning of the organs? There should be extra space under the eyes for the necessary overflow of fluids. If the skin has been tightened too much, the toxins can come into the eyes instead of pooling below them, thus adversely affecting the eyes. People who surgically remove the bags may end up with problems of the eyes, ears, teeth, nose, lips, and tongue. Instead, proper cleaning of the liver and kidneys will usually make the bags disappear.

WRINKLES AND BLEMISHES

Many people believe that wrinkles are based on the condition of the facial skin. This is only a small part of the truth. A better understanding is that the whole body has an energetic circuitry that connects all the different parts. Each wrinkle indicates a blockage in one of the marmas somewhere inside in the body.

For example, wrinkles around the eyes indicate that the navel marma is blocked. When the three important marmas in the navel are blocked, the area around the eyes is affected. Wrinkles on the upper part of the lips indicate a blockage in the *nabhi* marma of the second chakra. Wrinkles on the forehead or on the chin indicate that the energy is blocked in the stomach marma. There are nine marmas on the stomach. Wrinkles on the chin, or a swollen chin, can also be connected to shoulder marmas.

Other external disruptions indicate internal imbalances. Blemishes on the forehead can be a sign of blockage of the marmas located at the solar plexus. Inflammation underneath the cheek or jaw can mean blockage of the navel marmas. Large pores on the cheeks, or inflammation of the cheeks, indicates blockage of the nerve marmas. Discoloration on the nose indicates a blockage in the heart marma. There is one marma as big as the palm of a hand on the chest. A red, swollen nose is the outward sign of trouble in the arterial marmas.

Feelings and Emotions

We all have feelings and emotions. The whole balance of the body is naturally self-regulating when we can express our feelings without disturbing others. To have this ability, we need to stimulate our own mind and body from time to time. That stimulation is best when well-balanced. Even simple social pleasures such as seeing a movie, having a good conversation, or enjoying the fun of a social event can fulfill that need. Sharing emotions with someone helps us to clear the heart connection, but expressing our love and feelings is also stimulating for ourselves.

The feelings and emotions happening inside the body are reflected on a person's marmas. For those who study Marma Science from Dhanur Veda, it is important to know about this so as not to miss any clue that might reveal an opponent's intentions, such as when the opponent is getting ready to attack. Very careful attention must be paid to facial movements, even when a person is smiling. Nearly imperceptible movements — like some part of his face becoming strained, tightened, or loosened — means that his adrenal gland is already starting to produce adrenaline and he is going to raise his arm.

That kind of careful, scientific study is necessary if one wants to become a skillful martial artist. More than physical strength is necessary; intellectual strength allows us to use our brain to figure out what the other person is trying to do. Instead of trying to attack and break the opponent, we can simply move out of the way. That is one of the wise principles of Indian martial art.

S. S. of San Francisco, California has this opinion:
I'm a psychiatrist. I practice mainstream psychiatry. For the past two years, I've also been doing Ayur Vedic consultations. Ayur Veda is of course the traditional Indian system of medicine. I've used Joseph's products, and I've also gone through the Healing Program with him. The Healing Program is, of course, much more powerful than using the creams and the teas. I found an immense amount of changes to occur in a very short amount of time. I've been trained in body-oriented psychotherapy, which actually looks at how the body is responding to various emotional traumas. I found that the Rejuvenation Program really helps bring repressed emotions to the surface very quickly, so that they can be dealt with and gotten rid of, which is healing as opposed to treating an illness, which is what much of psychiatry does through giving medications. That's not to say that medications can't give benefit and help alleviate suffering in people, but it doesn't really heal anything, whereas things like body-oriented psychotherapy and Joseph's program, is actually healing, in my opinion.

I've also had clients who have used the products, the creams and the teas, and I've found them to be very good also at getting to the emotional toxins and sometimes physical toxins that are underlying the illnesses that these people have. As I said before, the creams and the teas are not as powerful as the Rejuvenation Program, but for most people, they're quite adequate to bring out enough toxins that they can deal with. Sometimes I've had to have people even back off from the program a little bit, until they can ready themselves and be prepared to go back into the program, because they need some time to deal with the emotions that are coming up. If it's physical toxins, to get those physical toxins out of the body.

So all in all, I'd say that something very profound is happening when you use these products, and it's in the realm of healing rather than just treatment of illnesses. There's resistance, and in psychotherapy, when you're pointing out something to somebody, an emotional problem they're unaware of, they're unconscious of, they will resist even going into that area, unconsciously. It's the same with the treatment. I've had clients who very much didn't want to go through the treatment when they saw that it was going to unleash those emotions. It is important for some people to be in therapy, to be able to work through those emotions because they can be traumatic. They were traumatic to begin with and they can be traumatic when they come back out. But once they're dealt with, then as I say, the person's life just goes up another notch and they feel so much better.

I think that going through the Healing Program is one of the most powerful services that you offer, and it really can help bring these emotions out, help people function much better in life, bring up things into their consciousness that they were unaware of, things that were really blocking them in the path to success, or whatever they wanted to do in life. And in a very short amount of time, too, which is a big advantage. Sometimes, somatic psychotherapy takes years and years and years, whereas you can accomplish a lot in a week or less with the Healing Program

Digestion

A guest in someone's home in India is treated like royalty. The common courtesies — politeness and basic manners of how to speak to people and treat guests — contribute to healthy digestion. Old India must have known that saying something indelicate to a person can have a physical effect, especially before a meal. When someone is upset before and during a meal, it can cause disorder in the digestive organs.

Indians eat food with their hands, which often surprises Westerners. What does it mean to eat with the hands? There is nothing dirty about it. The food we take inside ourselves remakes our body. We have to love that food, to feel it and touch it. The body's energy field is connected to the universal energy, which is connected to our physical energy. Energy is all connected. When we touch our food, the five fingers connect to the five organs and assist the organs by relaying the message contained in the energy of the food. The organs respond to this energy and function appropriately.

Furthermore, Indian food contains spices which are calculated to correspond with the organs of our body — a special energy to interconnect with our own energy in the body. The tongue is connected to the brain. When we put food in our mouth, the tongue analyzes the food and immediately produces the taste which allows the brain to decide how much fuel to produce to digest the food coming to the stomach. As we chew, the organs are preparing to process the food. The brain is analyzing the many tiny bits of food on the tongue. It is quite interesting, this computer in the brain.

The brain directly gives the order to the digestive organs, "Gall bladder, produce this amount of bile." Bile is so powerful and acidic that food has to be protected by the saliva until it gets into the stomach. Saliva protects all the vitamins, minerals, proteins, nutrients, and such. Food breaks down when it gets into the stomach. After that, the process continues in the intestines where the nutritional elements are absorbed.

All this discussion is going on between the brain, the organs, and the rest of the body while the food is traveling through the alimentary canal. The food is actually pushed through, section by section. While the food is moving through the intestines, the brain decides, "This vitamin has to go to this place; that mineral has to go to that place. Too much calcium! No need to send it there. He needs some minerals and vitamins for those tissues. More oxygen for the skin. Send extra to the part with an injury." The intestines are covered with arteries and veins which carry on the absorption. There is no waste. Almost everything is useful, but the brain will decide if there are some things that are not needed, so those parts are sent through the intestine and into the colon.

There is also another player in this drama — the gastric acid and gas which push the foodstuff through the intestines. We know the gas is really pushing because some of it comes back into the stomach. Bile and gas have to come together as they are synergistically connected. Otherwise, gastric disorders happen.

Digestive imbalances are the most common problem today. Imbalances cause waste to remain inside the intestines instead of being pushed from the body. Constipation results. Everything gets stuck in the stomach and intestines. The brain does not know what to do. The body does not absorb anything from the intestine, so the body does not get any good building blocks in the form of nutrients. All this food bound together is dangerous. Acid helps digestion, but it often remains with the food, causing the bile to be reabsorbed into the system. **Skin problems are the end result**.

Think about skin cancer. The sun has existed for at least 150 million years. We first noticed skin problems developing one hundred and twenty years ago, and now we consider the sun to be a threat. Everybody says, "Don't go in the sun." What people do not realize is that just a small amount of bile absorbed back into the tissues due to improper digestion becomes part of the tissues and layers of skin. When we go into the sun and begin to sweat, the acid starts to surface and burn the skin. There should be no acid in the tissues. Acid needs to be completely cleansed from the food during digestion. The intestines continue to absorb the acid until the tract is cleaned and healthy assimilation is restored. Otherwise, acidity continues to build in all areas of the body, causing weakness. When a person sweats, the sweat comes out through the skin, bringing with it the acid and bile. In combination with the heat of the sun, the abnormal new tissue becomes skin cancer.

Only the good elements of food should be absorbed into the body, especially into the bone. Bone is adversely affected by the wrong intestinal fluids, such as when acid completely destroys calcium in a very short time. Then bone is rebuilt with this unhealthy calcium which is mixed with bile. The afflictions resulting from improper digestion could be prevented if we recognized this series of events. When the bile goes back into the bodily tissues, even the bone marrow is damaged.

Skin and Acidity

Most human skin problems result from acidity. Skin damage, skin cancer, skin freckles, oily skin, skin thinness, and tiredness all come from the acidity which has been created in the stomach. For example, oily skin can result from acidity. Perspiration from the sweat glands is supposed to help moisturize the skin, and the oil from the sebaceous glands is supposed to help lubricate the skin. When they become contaminated with acidity, the sebaceous glands become weakened, and an overbalance of oil production is the consequence. The skin can become dry for the same reason — weakness of the sweat glands. These glands are designed to produce within themselves the natural liquid for the skin. But we are drying out our skin by applying abrasive substances that weaken it from the outside.

What is skin and how does it work? Skin is our coat of protection. It is fighting every day to defend us against bacteria, viruses, or whatever external intruders might try to enter the body. **Skin is the largest organ of the body and is responsible for its protection.** It is managed and maintained by proper timing in supplying new cells and removing old cells. Renewal and exfoliation are naturally-regulated processes in a healthy body. When acidity is mixed with the food we eat, this acidity will spread throughout the body and enter the body's cells. New cells are then built from the weak cells. That means acidic cells will go into the formation of the skin.

Many people think the solution to cleaning the skin is to remove layers off the top, as with skin peeling. But taking off layers of the skin is not the solution; it only weakens the skin again and again. In some ways, of course, peeling can smooth the skin, but it is based on the false assumption that there are plenty of new layers and that those new layers are healthy.

All kinds of fruits naturally contain fruit acid. God has made fruit with so many different components. There are minerals and vitamins. Those acids which are inside the fruit are protected so that when we eat the fruit, we do not normally feel the acid content. Still, when we eat an orange or drink orange juice, we are often affected by the acidity. Then scientists discovered that this acid had an effect on the skin. It may help to thin the skin, but it is not something that can bring out or stimulate our inner energy. In fact, when the fruit acid mixes with the acid that is already inside us and on our skin, it corrodes the skin.

In my homeland, my sister used to cut a lemon and put it on the corner of her elbow or any rough area. Lemon can smooth an area of the skin, from the very little acid that is present naturally. The small amount of acid in that fruit is protected and helps to activate that fruit when it is eaten.

Nature prepares these fruits so that they are chemically balanced for our digestion. When we strip them of their natural protective coating, they become powerful acids. When the fruit acid is isolated and that concentrated form is put on the skin, the skin can be permanently damaged. Is there any real difference between fruit acid and any other powerful acid applied to the skin?

Imagine an apple, which is alive. What happens when the outside skin is removed? Naturally, all kinds of bacteria can come inside the apple. The same thing happens when we harshly exfoliate our skin. Instead, what we need to do is cleanse the skin *internally* and thereby control the chemical reactions occurring on the skin as well as within the body. Remember, clearing the blockages is the way to cleanse.

Toxicity and Health Disorders

Dry skin, oily skin, combination skin. What is normal skin?

These days, it is rare to see normal skin. Most skin is predominantly dry or oily. One of the most common changes I have seen is that some parts of the face, especially on the cheek area or the nose, have bigger pores than other parts of the face. Over-inflammation of the tissue produces water in the skin, and the pores of the skin become enlarged.

Why does that happen? Inside us, toxins are being created in the stomach, intestines, and in different parts of the body. They cannot pass through the internal mechanisms properly because the energy in the marmas is blocked. Healthy marmas regulate the tissue functions, which carry these toxins through the systems of elimination. When some of the systems are impaired, the toxins that are not removed by the intestine or colon are kept in a temporary storage area. Toxins cannot be stored for longer than a certain time, so eventually the storage becomes permanent. One result of this toxicity is formation of cellulite.

The same is true for toxins that have been created from emotional imbalances. Large pores develop on the skin of the nose area. If the toxins are created in the stomach and intestinal area, large pores will develop on the cheek area. If the toxins are created in the colon area, large pores will be seen underneath the chin. Hormonal imbalance creates breakouts underneath the chin. If toxins are created from the sexual organs, gall bladder, adrenal gland, liver, or kidney, the pores on both sides of the ears become bigger. All the color starts to change with the filling of the veins on the side of the face or on the nose. The cause of this coloration is that all the toxins cannot go through the liver because the liver is already toxic.

The liver is our purifying factory. A thousand times more waste is coming into the liver than it can process, so it simply throws the toxins out. The liver has the capacity to send toxins to other parts of the body. The skin, as the largest organ of elimination, will throw off an enormous amount of toxins.

When the paths of elimination are releasing toxins, they create open pores in different parts of the body so the skin can throw off the toxins. The first place affected is the face. Other places are on the thigh areas, where cellulite forms. Some people may have noticed that if they press on the outer parts of their legs, they will experience pain and bruising can occur. If they exercise, they will see that there are blue or brownish marks on different areas all over the legs. On white skin, there can be brownish marks. For dark skin, there can be varicose veins. This bruising is caused by the deposits of the toxins which the body is trying to get out through the junctions of the marmas. When those junctions are blocked discoloration will occur.

For the most part, the release valves are in the main marma areas. When people have problems with their stomach, they will experience pain on the knee or on the upper part of the calf because the toxins concentrate there. The body always has ways to adapt – extra areas that are utilized when the body has no way to discard the toxins through the stomach and intestines. There the toxins can remain for perhaps a week or two. Beyond that time, the body has to find a solution — a way to release the toxins. What happens is that the skin is destroyed in that area. It becomes slowly weaker and weaker until the toxins can get out. After a massage, one can see some of the skin color change within a day or two as toxins are coming out through the skin.

For men, acidity builds up in the solar plexus area, which becomes toxic and can be destroyed. Whenever they eat food, it comes up to their vital chest area; they have acidity problems which affect the heart marma, one of the most important marmas. The heart marma controls feelings and emotions. When there is toxicity in this specific marma, we can become emotional and nervous. Sometimes when emotional problems occur in a man, the chest hairs turn gray and his body immediately starts to age. When there is obstruction in the heart area, the nose can be very thick and red; there is also redness in the face and neck. Loss of hair at the front of the head is another indication. Men's beauty, vitality, and health are at stake. Healthy strength is necessary for a person to be able to defend himself and generate power from specific areas of the body.

For a woman, acidic congestion will show up as breast cancer, breast tumors, and breast calcification. When toxic congestion exists over time, the calcification or acidity goes into the lymphatic nodes. Bits of calcium get caught in the breast and become thicker and thicker until a doctor says, "We found a small tumor." In fact, fat tissue or calcium build-up can be eliminated gradually by controlling the level of acidity and applying special herbs to the breasts. In India, herbs were used to modify the breasts and make them more beautiful. After delivery, women used to apply an herbal cream to their breasts to make them shorter and firmer. Some of the herbs were given internally and some externally. Together they worked to remedy this problem.

Women can also have the same problems as men. The acidity that creates calcium disorders can spread to the shoulder area, face, eyes, teeth, nails, ears, and hair, causing more stress. Ears, eyes, and teeth show the damage; hair can have split ends, become thin, and fall out.

Other ailments I have studied in people are the host of arthritic problems, backaches, headaches, sinus problems, and migraines. If digestive disorders are treated properly, we can remove any kind of arthritis and even restore the five elements, i.e., the five sense organs. Health of the ears, eyes, nose, mouth, and skin can be restored in a matter of two to three months.

Even dental problems can result from digestive disorders or blockages of marmas in different parts of the stomach area. What happens is that acid from the stomach area travels to the mouth and weakens the protective enamel of the teeth. For stomach problems, I have seen people take medicine to dilute the acid, but this is not the solution. Then they no longer have sufficient acid and bile in the stomach to digest their food. They also lose energy, which impairs the body's ability to produce more bile, and they are left with a deficiency. Treatment begins with the adrenal gland.

This gland can create a sensitivity, a weakness in the marmas. Some are born with it, and others develop it. When the marmas are treated properly, the whole digestive system can return to a balanced condition.

There are some marmas in the calf area that are connected to the spleen and gall bladder. When they get blocked, an acidity disorder occurs. When there is already abnormal acidity and a person sits in one position for a long time, the volume of that acidity is doubled. This, in turn, causes stomach disorders and peptic ulcers. Sedentary people often have inflamed, sensitive skin, which is due, in part, to abnormal acidity.

Hair Loss, Thinning, and Graying

What is hair? Hair is the waste of the bone, or excess calcium rejected out of the body in the form of hair and the nails on the hands and feet. Mostly the hair is in nine different parts of the human body: head, ears, nose, above the lips, anus, genitals, armpits, plus the chest and navel (for men). These are the main sense organs of the body in men and women. Any sensitivity or frustration, blockages or imbalances in the human body, mind, and soul can affect all these places, which are based on the bone marmas that connect to different parts of the body. Any imbalance in the stomach will affect the calcium that forms the hair with too much growth or malfunction of the growth.

How does this happen? From the food we are eating, we absorb calcium, minerals, vitamins, protein — everything necessary to build and maintain the body. Food goes into the stomach. The bile coming into the stomach helps to break down what is in the food. After that, the digested food enters the intestines, where the arteries absorb and carry the digested substances to different parts of the body.

Calcium builds up the bones. Sometimes, when we eat food, there is too much calcium content. Excess calcium is discharged first as nails. The total calcium from the food we have taken in will be distributed to the nine parts of the body. Because of blockages, our body sometimes miscalculates the exact amount going to different parts. This is compensated by the rejection of the excess calcium which becomes the hair in the different parts of the body. Sometimes, while passing through the body after being rejected, this calcium gets lodged in the lungs, shoulders, kidneys, or stomach, and forms calcium deposits. It all depends on which marmas are not activated properly or which marmas are blocked in the body.

Hair is excess calcium left after building the bones. If you want to test this idea, eat more calcium-producing food for one month. Your hair stylist will say, "Wow, your hair is growing fast." Try cashews, almonds, pistachios, beans, hormone-free milk, etc. If your body is in a balanced state, when you have a lack of calcium you will naturally feel drawn to eating the corrective foods.

Now you may ask, "So I am eating all these nuts, why am I still losing my hair?" Here comes the part about our emotions and frustrations. Every emotion affects different parts of the body. It depends on what type of thinking we do or which part of the brain we are utilizing to think. For example, if we are very intellectual, we will be using the front of the brain in the forehead area. The top of the head is more active when a person worries about everything or is anxious about business. In the back of the head, in the little round depression, there can be blockage from a lack of spirituality. Oversensitivity or extreme intelligence in people can be related to a blockage in the throat area. Emotions can block the throat marma and the throat marma can disturb the endocrine system.

These are some examples, but these concepts comprise a huge subject. In this way, the emotions affect the hair, depending on which marmas are being blocked. Even though we eat the correct foods for calcium, when we have those emotional thoughts, an acidic imbalance happens in the stomach that may destroy, dilute, or weaken the calcium. Depending on what happens, it may thin our hair or turn it gray. If we are extremely emotional, we will get more gray hair. For example, if we worry too much, our hair may become thin. If we are confused or depressed, our hair may split or break. External application of proper herbal ingredients to stimulate the marmas can balance hair restoration within limits. I have personally helped dozens of people with completely bald heads to grow their hair back, although it requires permanent and constant balancing of the body.

Weight Gain

Weight gain can happen for many reasons, as we all know.

Gaining weight from food is the last thing I would target. Most of the weight gain I have seen is because people are lacking food for the mind and soul. I have talked about balancing the body, mind, and spirit at once. I know people who eat all different kinds of food and do not gain any weight. It has to do with the nature of the time they were born. Sensitivity and emotions have an effect at the time of our birth. Our brain is connected to the planets and stars. If we are born with a blockage, the positive side of the planets is not stimulating the energy which connects to our mind and soul. When we say soul, it could be the thyroid, digestive organs (such as the weakness of the adrenal gland), or any part of the endocrine system. The adrenal gland is part of the digestive organs, which include the spleen, pancreas, kidneys, gallbladder, liver, and adrenals.

All those parts are controlled by the marmas connected to each organ. The marmas are set with data, like computer memory, at the time of birth. If they get blocked at the time of birth, lack of activation occurs in the above-mentioned organs. This includes the reproductive organs. This can get very technical, but most of the thousands of clients I have treated have been eating perfectly balanced foods. I do not usually suggest a better diet because they are already eating well. Basically, I had to discover this concept of subtle causes of weight gain and apply it to people who visited me for their weight concerns. It has helped them to lose weight within a month. This I would call fulfilling the mind and soul — giving the right food to the mind and soul.

Basically, each of our organs has to be healthy and active. Only then do we feel interested in all kinds of nourishing food. Otherwise, we feel drawn to foods which may not be suitable. This does not mean it is bad food. All foods are good. For example, if our spleen and pancreas are weak or the marmas connected to those organs are not stimulated properly, we feel drawn to sugar, sweets, and acidic food. Avoiding that food does not prevent other addictions like smoking or alcohol. Basically, we have to release the blockage everywhere equally. One solution for craving too much sugar is to eat more rice and avoid wheat. Eating acidic food, such as processed tomatoes, is not recommended in this case, although fresh tomatoes may be good. The reason for eating rice instead of sugar is that rice has natural sugar, so the body can produce enough glucose for the spleen and pancreas to do their job.

Other imbalances in body chemistry can result from relationships or partnerships we have with other people, and the clothes and jewelry we wear. For some people, woolen clothing is not good. Of course, emotion, frustration, worry, anxiety, general stress, and ambition all contribute to weight gain. These are just a few of the myriad factors that can affect our weight.

> C. K. of Santa Monica, California, gave her professional opinion:
> I am an esthetician, specializing in skin care. The first thing I noticed was more energy. Then I saw my skin transform. It was softer, smoother and had greater elasticity. Cellulite decreased tremendously, and my skin tightened up. Actually, I lost inches without losing any weight and fit into my clothes much more attractively. My clients noticed the change and talked about a new glow radiating from my skin. Everyone wanted to know what I was doing.

> B. J. of San Francisco, California, experienced weight loss and firming:
> The benefits are terrific. I think the creams are great. They all work together in harmony. I don't have a lot of time to work on my face and do things with my body. I'm in and out. I'm a very busy person, and so it's wonderful that in just a few minutes, I'm ready to go with my day and I feel great.

> My friends notice the change and they've mentioned it to me. A friend asked me yesterday if I was growing new skin. I thought that was a terrific compliment to Joseph Kurian. When you start using the product, it puts you in a whole new frame of mind, and consequently, I find myself doing more. If I put on a body cream and I start exercising, and I get going, I've lost some weight. People have noticed. It's just amazing. I've said nothing, yet people come forward and asked me what I am doing these days because I look so much better. And I

have to say the only thing I've changed in my life is that I've added the Joseph Kurian products to my life. In the last thirty days, my skin has taken on a whole new texture, and it's been marvelous.

It's been just a transformation for me, and I wouldn't have believed it unless I tried it myself. But I've tried it myself and I have to honestly say, "It's a great product." It's the first time in a long time that I've actually started wearing sleeveless dresses. My arms look good; my legs look good. I've been out at the beach. My skin just feels better. It's not as dry. I can't say enough good things about the product.

Menstrual Problems and Menopause

Menstrual and menopause problems are very much related. A woman who has long-time menstrual problems tends to enter menopause earlier. Most menstrual problems are created from emotional disorders. How is this particular part of the body affected by the emotions? The soul, or spirit, is the endocrine system. The endocrine system is divided into the pituitary gland, thyroid, thymus, digestive organs, and reproductive organs. The pituitary produces the hormones, which have to be regularly supplied to the reproductive organs every cycle of the month. This flow can be blocked in daily life by general problems — frustrations, worries, anxieties, trauma, accidental injuries, surgical defects — and cause blockage of the marmas.

Marma blockage disrupts the digestive organs and thymus. When digestive organ disorders occur, the intestines and colon are affected. The colon is directly connected to the thymus and heart. How does colon disruption occur? There is a very important marma, the *manya marma*, located right under the ear. Each manya marma is connected to another marma in the center of each shoulder. The shoulder marmas are connected to the vagus nerve in the center of the shoulder blades. The shoulder marmas activate the colon and even the intestine. I have seen many people in my practice who were damaged at the time of birth, which disturbed the flow of energy to their colon and intestines. It also blocked the passage of energy from the shoulder to the chest and the chest to the reproductive organs.

> K. G. of Piedmont, California, is free of long-time discomfort:
> My healing for my back is wonderful, but there is something for which I am even more grateful. From the time I was thirteen, I had painful, long periods with a very irregular cycle. As I got older, my symptoms increased. I tried all kinds of herbs, acupuncture, muscle relaxers, vitamins, as well as every type of pain medication. Nothing helped and my periods were getting worse all the time. There is no way to put into words how this healing has changed my life.

Menstrual problems in women are similar to prostate problems in men. Most men have blockage of the manya marma. This is partially caused by wearing tight clothing such as buttoned shirts and neckties, similar to the effect that wearing constrictive undergarments and tight-fitting nylons has in causing cellulite in women. Throughout European history, one can observe fashions that fit tightly around the neck. Think of Victorian blouses! Clothing designers were creating these fashions without understanding physiological energy passage.

There is often physical and mental blockage in the thymus. You may notice your shoulders become tight. If you rub your chest, you may feel pain there. You may even have congestion in the digestive organs. The spiritual side of the blockage is often in the neck area or thyroid. They are all interconnected with each other.

In India, after a woman's menstrual period begins, she wears herbal paste on the forehead, chest, and eyebrows to prevent problems that occur during puberty. This is one of the preventive disciplines. The Night Cream I have created is based on these principles. Many of the menstrual difficulties have been greatly alleviated by my programs.

Some of the herbal combinations I have created, for example, *mastabhi*, stimulate the manya, *sthana* (thymus or chest) and nabhi marmas. These are three of the most important areas in the human body where body, mind, and spirit join together. Once blockages are released in all three places, keep repeating the resonant sound

AA - OO - MA and this will help to keep stimulating these locations constantly. There is a saying that certain sounds have endless meaning. All of this requires proper instruction.

Our human lifespan covers 120 years, divided by the 7th, 14th, 21st, 42nd, and 84th years. These are the growing and weakening times of life. For example, the first seven years are the general growth of childhood. The next seven years, the body starts to produce hormones up to the age of fourteen. Fourteen to twenty-one, there are other changes. When a person reaches the age of twenty-one, the entire body, mind, and soul are permanently built for their entire lifespan. After that, there is only cell replacement in our body, no actual growth. The body is already built and ready to go. From the age of twenty-one to forty-two years, our body remains active, vital, and healthy.

After the age of forty-two, changes start to happen. Those twenty-one years prior have the most stress as we work hard and use our maximum energy for creating our purpose. After that, our body starts to weaken, our mind and nervous system slow down, the endocrine system functions more slowly. One who starts to take proper care at this age, helping the body replace cells in time, can help the cells to hold the information properly everywhere.

This means we need to release the blockage of the energy constantly so that the endocrine system can function and the hormones can be produced until the age of ninety. A man or woman can replace their hormones and remain young. There are women who have corrected blockages and started their menstrual period again at the age of sixty-five after it had stopped before fifty. Prevention of menopause means replacing the cells in every part of the body equally so that one can balance their hormone production.

CHAPTER SEVEN

Herbs and Marma Teas

The first system one has to follow to relieve marma blockages is to use herbs in a simple process of stimulation. This particular knowledge of herbal cleansing has been all but lost to the modern world. The healing aspects have nearly vanished from spiritual and religious teachings.

Formulas for growing, gathering, preparing, and blending herbs and spices have been passed down through families in an oral tradition, from master to disciple, or carefully recorded on palm leaf manuscripts. These palm leaves were themselves treated with herbs to prevent their deterioration, and the precious knowledge written on them is known as the *Marma Sutras*.

Please see figures 20 and 21 in the center of this book
[Palm leaf scrolls]

The precise herbal formulations of the Marma Sutras are designed according to the laws of universal energy to produce the desired result on specific marma blockages. Every aspect of herbal preparation must follow the original directions. The herbs are picked according to very strict rules regarding factors such as the planetary influences. Accuracy is of the utmost importance, both in the quantity and methodology.

Stimulating the specific energy centers can be accomplished with the use of very special herbal combinations. As our light body resonates to a higher frequency than does our physical body, so do herbs emit higher frequencies than other plants. Herbs have more harmonic vibrations in their auras than do other plants, making them more electrical and informational.

The photosynthesis they conduct transmutes the light of the sun and stars into the finest nourishment for our physical and psychological well-being. When herbs are combined with spiritual respect, there is a new synergistic energy produced. These herbal energetics interact with the electromagnetic currents in the body, serving to stimulate them sufficiently to clear the blockages from the pathways. The body's own current is then free to flow without interruption.

Ideally, herbs are ingested as teas or are applied externally through skin creams. The transdermal herbal extracts in the creams permeate the skin and enter the body. The skin is the largest organ of the body, yet only in recent years has Western medicine begun to utilize this organ as a vehicle for medication. In the marma tradition of India, it has long been the preferred method. However, in some cases it may be more effective to stimulate the marmas with herbal formulations through the digestive organs. This is why some herbs are taken as teas. Simultaneously, synergistically, the teas and creams provide herbal energy that penetrates the body's energy. The subtle body is of a finer texture than the physical. Clearing the marma channels reaches the fundamental level, where transformation occurs more rapidly and disharmonies are dissolved.

Quality of the Herbs

Why is the quality of the herbs so important? At the refined level of physiology of the marmas, information must pass between the cells of the herbs and the cells of the body. Both are living entities, and we can say that they communicate at the cellular level. With the precise molecular distillation of the plant essences, the body can recognize the nutrients it needs and will automatically accept these nutrients directly, allowing the digestive system to gain deep rest.

Which herbs we use is not as important as *how* we process the herbs to retain the vital quality of prana. Very strict rules about gathering, preparing, combining, and administering the herbs are employed to guard the prana. The herbs are grown in specified terrain within set guidelines concerning elevation and access to water and heat. There are certain times of year when they are each picked — and only then. Some must be harvested in the middle of a full moon night. Every detail is supervised, even to the hour in which they are picked and by whom they are gathered. The people who pick the herbs must themselves be purified and must wear neither clothes nor shoes while they pick. The work is done in seclusion to maintain purity.

The preparation of organic herbs takes years. Just as a vineyard takes a long time in preparation for the grapevines, so does the care of the plantation take time for the precious herbs to retain the energy of the sun. A very special way of traditional processing teaches that the herbs have to be dried in the sun for 41 days, 90 days, 180 days, 212 days, or even 1644 days. Drying the plants in the sun helps them to absorb the positive planetary energy of each of the planets. By absorbing the solar energy, the herbs and spices are fortified. By tradition, only when every detail is correct can true benefits be realized.

The energy of the sun, combined with the live molecular energy of the herbs, is contained in the plant extracts. The energy in the herbs has to be properly aligned – the combination has to be correct in every aspect to create an electrical energy that stimulates the life force current in the human body. Using the exact process handed down for centuries ensures that the powerful energy of the plant at the molecular level is released for use by the human constitution.

Combinations of Herbs

Based on extensive research, I have formulated Marma Skincare products to accommodate specific needs of the skin in the modern environment. However, it would be unwise simply to adapt these formulas to the convenience of our times. Rather, we must acknowledge the ancient ways and follow the prescriptions as they have been passed along to us. Our well-being is too important to compromise.

In one respect, there is nothing special about these herbs individually. The properties of different botanicals are familiar to us; they are all available in the Indian kitchen. They are the same herbs and spices we actually ingest with food. If we go into the kitchen, take a piece of black pepper and chew it, we will start to notice after a while that our body is heating up. If we boil a piece of cardamom to make a tea and drink it, we will feel that it is stimulating a sense of happiness. Coriander taken internally helps to correct digestion. These are all eliciting responses from the subtle energy in our body.

Please see figure 22 in the center of this book
[Botanical Blends]

It is the proper combination of spices that provides the secret of beauty. Each of the plants holds its own special qualities. Examples of herbs in Marma Skincare are:

Hibiscus: One of the most beautiful flowers in any tropical country, it is used for cooling the skin and giving it a silken texture. In Kerala, hibiscus is freshly ground and applied to the skin. Even wearing the flower behind the ear has a cooling effect on the body.
Holy Basil: Considered sacred in India for its ability to open the heart to love, devotion, and compassion. Strengthens the immune system.
Lotus root and flower: Held in high regard for beauty aspects, lotus is used in the temples of India. It brings incredible smoothness to the skin by helping cells to rebuild rapidly and exfoliate naturally.
Saffron: In its original form, saffron is too strong for the skin, but specially distilled it penetrates gently with a very powerful, stimulating effect. Popular in Indian cuisine, it is used for the beauty of the skin and to increase the aura. Revitalizes tissues and the blood.
Sandalwood: Soothes inflammations. Cools the body, calms the mind, promotes meditation, devotion, and intelligence.

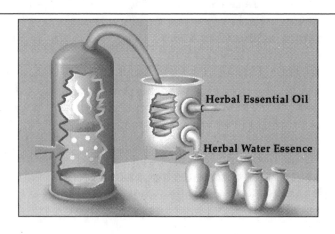

The blend is a synergy. The quality within the herb that interacts with the marmas is its pranic energy. That is what must be captured. The passage of electric current inside the body will help to replace all the old cells and bring new cells to the surface of the skin. It is not the herbs directly that are effecting these results. It is that synergistically they are all connected to each other in a rejuvenating process.

When pranic energy starts to absorb properly and circulate all over the body, the nutrients from food combine with it and the energy which is already inside us starts to activate. This is the optimum level of functioning. The body naturally seeks homeostasis. With adequate stimulation and without the interference of blockages, we can regain our natural balance.

The combinations in the food recipes (see Recipes, Part Four) are somewhat different from those of the herbal recipes. These same herbal blends, my master told me, were applied to the bodies of kings and queens in ancient India so they could radiate the charisma that commanded respect. My master said, "It may look to you to be very simple, but if you do it the right way, it can give great good to the whole world. I have seen that there is a capability in you to invent an incredible system to benefit everyone in the world."

We would all be wise to have respect for antiquity. The ancient beliefs that obey natural laws contain the knowledge of rejuvenation for an individual in the context of his or her environment. The system of Marma Skincare is based on the timeless, precious concepts of natural energy and is adapted to our modern lifestyle for our convenience.

Birth of an Idea

For two thousand years, people have traveled far to obtain the fine quality herbs and spices of Kerala. Renowned for their use as delicious seasonings, herbal teas and tonics, as well as a variety of other applications, Kerala spices have found their way around the world. It was fascinating for me to discover how penetrating the herbs and spices in seasoning can be. That is what made me think about using the same spices that our family used — sandalwood, saffron, and turmeric — for skincare. I thought, "Why cannot these herbs be applied on the skin by everyone?" I tried to adapt the ingredients and took the distillation of the aromatic effect from the spices. I was interested to see whether the results internally would follow once the combination was applied externally. I discovered it indeed had the same effect.

The next logical step was to develop the same system internally in tea form. First I tried a certain combination of spices as a tea and drank that. I would bring the ingredients with me to the West because the same foods are not available here as in India. I continued to refine the blends, keeping in mind my goal of maintaining the integrity of the original formulas. At the same time, I adjusted them according to the influences of contemporary climates.

When we take herbal teas internally to complement the application of the creams externally, there is an excitation of the whole body and aura. It has an excellent effect. This discovery is what created Marma Skincare. More than simply offering beauty, it is life-enhancing. What is actually occurring is that the energy inside us, which is the entire chakra system, is waking up. The chakra system is waking up, which increases the aura inside and around us.

When we use the same extracts externally, that same aura is attracted to our skin. The effect is very fast because there is a connection made within our energy system. The electromagnetic current is like electricity. When we turn the electricity on inside and outside our house, the whole area is flooded with light. The result of a stronger electromagnetic current in us is clear, shining skin with an auric glow.

Marma Teas or Tablets

According to the ancient concepts, it is absolutely essential to balance the energy system of the body. This energy balance goes to the fundamental level of the anatomy, which is the subtle level. It goes beyond a person's age or race, because our body, mind, and spirit are related to the universal energy system. We use energy every day for things like computers and telecommunications. Why not use it to enhance our own beauty?

The set of Marma Teas consists of **Stimulating Morning Tea** and **Cleansing Evening Tea**. Each box contains a month's supply of teas. One cup of tea in the morning and one in the evening is all that is needed. The teas help to stimulate the marmas during the day and relax them during the night. We need increased energy levels for our daily activities and a gentle, cleansing energy at night to support the bodily processes during sleep.

The beauty of the herbal teas or tablets is that specific blends taken internally have the power to balance the stomach chemistry. The stomach is the factory of the entire body. If there is acidity in the stomach, it destroys the calcium which is absorbed from food, so the bones become malnourished. There is nothing more detrimental, as that deficiency affects consciousness itself. Calcium is also one of the materials of muscle fiber. All the tissues are interconnected.

Of course, a healthy diet has to be properly maintained. I have seen many people who have tried fad diets such as low-fat foods and have totally lost their muscular power. Repeated use of the Marma Teas offers thorough cleansing of the physiology and activates the body's own rejuvenating mechanisms. The energetic bolstering permits the body to devote more resources to rebuilding tissues rather than to defending itself in an exhausting effort. Blockages are gradually released, and healthy cells are created.

> R. G. of Minneapolis, Minnesota, recognizes positive results:
> My mental clarity is outstanding. I feel more emotionally grounded. My spiritual being is more grounded. It seems like my body, mind and spirit are all made lighter at the same time. I'm more accepting of my surroundings and appreciate life. I'm calmer, more at peace. It's just wonderful. My whole being has improved tremendously since doing these teas. I see a profound difference in my being - in being who I truly am - the authentic me. I'm very delighted with the products. I think they're just amazing.

Benefits of Marma Herbs

According to Marma Science, holding a blockage in the body for more than three months will cause a minimum of three years of aging. Conversely, when the blockage is released, there is a gain of at least three years of longevity. Because the body tends to maintain old habits, it is essential to engage in a program that will assist the body in stabilizing itself.

An auxiliary benefit of the herbs is that they enable the body to absorb more oxygen in the blood. This brings increased well-being and a feeling of control over our bodies. Providing the opportunity for the body to rebuild gives us the chance to wake up to the psychological aspects of our situations. People are pleased to find that these herbal energetics manifest positive results, such as making the body more flexible and muscular. There is a natural inclination to eat less and have increased natural energy. Toxins are broken down and released while we continue in our daily activities.

Powerful yet subtle, the herbs cleanse and nourish the internal system. Applying the marma creams brings out the glow of energy and also prevents the toxins from becoming reabsorbed into the body. Clients notice healthier hair, a fresher, silkier complexion, improved skin tone, clearer eyes, and stronger nails. Digestion improves and breathing becomes easier. Even improvements in dental quality have been noted. The hormonal system is revitalized, and there is a greater ability to manage stress. People feel calm and able to make decisions with more ease. They are better able to maintain a calm certainty, even during difficult times. Meditation becomes a natural process. The mirror of the face and skin beautifully reflects internal health and well-being.

The formulations I have designed have been used by hundreds of people for years, and they have seen the benefits of the natural rejuvenative powers.

> L. K. of Huntington Beach, California, has used my creams, oils, and teas:
>
> Last month I began the second round of the 7-month program — WOW! My younger sister is so impressed, she has just started with you. I have always had very sensitive and dry skin, and have been very allergy prone. Now, the women at cosmetics counters comment on my beautiful skin. I am 48 and this is a first! But more so, I can feel the internal difference. I have moved from being rather shy, uncertain and fearful in life to a whole new level of confidence. I have more energy than I ever imagined. My husband (of 28 years) and I are more in love than ever.

Chapter Eight

Marma Skincare

The face ages for two reasons. One is our internal health; since the marmas on the face are connected to the digestive system, the face will show any difficulties that exist there. The other is that dead cells are not removed in time and, therefore, new cells are not called in to replace them in time. Dead cells are like any biological waste; it is the function of the veins to carry them away.

A common misunderstanding is that skin cells are "fed" with topical applications. The biology of the skin is actually the reverse of this concept. Skin cells are nourished from the inside with a combination of food from the stomach and intestines and pranic energy from the breath. Given the fact that skin cells on the surface of the epidermis will die in five days time and are already in the natural process of exfoliation, feeding them is really not possible.

Dead skin cells accumulate as the natural exfoliation process slows down. Once the flow of energy is blocked, the physiology does not receive the stimulation it needs to replace the old cells with new cells. Toxins typically exit through the liver, kidney, urine, or skin. Old cells cannot go back into the liver; they can only go out through the skin. When there is a healthy rate of exfoliation, the liver is free to process more efficiently and keep the skin clear. The marmas regulate this removal system.

Now that you have been exposed to much of the history and background of Marma Science and beauty, this chapter outlines the structure of easy-to-use methods for incorporating the knowledge into your daily life. In other words, we know that marma health is desirable, but how does one achieve these benefits, especially without being schooled in specific disciplines like Dhanur Veda?

Stimulating the facial marmas with precious herbal formulas will correct digestive problems over time. The face will reflect health and vitality, bringing out inner as well as outer beauty. People will say, "You are glowing! You look vibrant!" The God-given life force in each of us is greatly enhanced and the positive life energy appears as a strong aura, a glowing complexion, a shining personality, and an enthusiastic outlook. This can happen for everyone.

Cell replacement in a healthy individual occurs in a natural, rhythmic cycle. The vital energy goes through the nerves; the nerves stimulate the arteries and veins; the veins carry the old cells away as the arteries supply the new cells. Old cells disappear as the body's elimination process discards them. New cells form the fresh, glowing skin of a good complexion.

While applying marma creams on the skin, the stimulus from the herbal energy excites the physiology to a more normal activity. The more parts of the body that are touched with the creams, the more electrical current is activated and the brighter the glow of the skin.

> M. D. of San Francisco, California, noticed good results just from the creams:
> I have noticed there is a visible difference in the veins on my face. They were noticeably visible. They've subsided. Every time I would get out of the shower or have a glass of wine, my face would get very flushed and red — right on my cheekbones. There is a big difference in the appearance of my skin and it's definitely softer. Something is happening or has happened in my system. And my energy level seems to be going up. It's subtle, but I do have more energy. I'm trying to be aware of all the changes going on in my body.

> G. V., a client from Ojai, California, had been trying glycolic acid:
> I am 55 and was starting to get crepey skin and laugh lines. I had tried glycolic acid treatments, but got bored

with it. Plus the lines were still there. I used Joseph's Day Cream and in two usages the lines almost totally disappeared. I do massage for a lady who works for a well-known company. I didn't tell her that I was using Joseph's cream, but she noticed the difference immediately. She looked at my face and said, 'What are you doing with your skin? It looks wonderful!' I use the cream every day now. It sounds strange, but I feel like tiny fingers are massaging my skin after I use it.

Beautifying the Aura

For five years I had concentrated on developing a correct system for herbal cleansing and stimulation. Then, some years ago, a very powerful psychic predicted, "You will create something which will be of help to everyone and will enable them to achieve a more spiritual beauty." Spiritual beauty. That is what he said — spiritual beauty. When I started to think about what that might mean, I understood that the aura is the electromagnetic field which is inside us and around us. When these herbal potions are applied externally, they have the power to bring the electromagnetic energy through the skin, which illuminates it and gives it a glow. The light inside us connects with the extracts of herbs and spices, which open up the blockages in the aura of the body. The light of life energy starts to comes through all over the skin and creates a special charisma in a person. This is what is meant by 'spiritual beauty.'

When we awaken the energy of the marmas, we are clearing the universal channels of energy. The path to God is open, and the connection to universal energy is made easily. The marmas are of God. They are thoughts to connect to God. Once we clear the marmas, God helps us to continue clearing out in order for God to come in. So Marma Science is beyond thinking or beyond anything on the earth. To wake up this energy system, we need to follow the principles of universal energy. When the flow of vital energy within the physiology gains maximum efficiency, we have physical well-being, mental strength, emotional satisfaction, and spiritual fulfillment. When the marmas are not properly stimulated, planetary destiny bestowed at birth is not fulfilled. *Raja Yogum* means a person has the luck to be a king. Without the proper care of the marmas, the same person can be a street cleaner.

It is a common belief that the shining beauty of women comes simply from the application of creams on their skin. From the ancient discoveries, we know that beauty treatment is much, much more, which is why I developed the line of Marma Skincare. The energy of marma is universal and available to everyone. Plants absorb the energy from the sun and planets; humans absorb the energy from the plants, sun, and planets. Marma Skincare wakes up our energy one hundred times faster than any meditation or practice we do. A remarkable vibrancy occurs within minutes as our vital force is stimulated to a higher vibrational frequency. The triangle patterns open rapidly, increasing intuition, imagination, charisma, vibrancy, intelligence, and focus. The natural energy corrects and balances the systems of the body; love, passion, kindness, and creativity spontaneously spring to life. This shows we are connecting to the ultimate energy of God. People look at us differently, seeing us as somehow special.

Since ancient times, we have known that charisma is the most essential part of beauty. We say in India that the aura was discovered by yogis who practiced increasing its energy. When the aura is strengthened, the brain functions are augmented and health improves greatly. As the energy gradually changes in our body, the tridosha of endocrine, vascular, and nervous systems are balanced so that our organs function normally and become harmonized.

A person starts to glow in as little as three minutes after applying marma cream. The individual parts start to synchronize as the seven layers receive their respective nourishment. When using the marma creams, there are improvements in the glow of the aura during the first, second, and third weeks. The herbal ingredients penetrate the skin to internally repair the intersections of veins and arteries, as well as tissues. The energy in the creams will go as fast as the electric current of the body moves, so the effects are dramatic.

The Problem with Some "Natural" Products

The medicinal purpose of transdermal patches is effective, not for the health of the skin, but to deliver a concentrated derivative of a natural substance. I would never suggest keeping any strong, aromatic oil on the skin for more than half an hour. Because the skin needs to breathe, even sesame oil should not be left on any longer than twenty minutes. Some aromatic oils are so powerful that the eventual effect on the skin is to weaken nerves, arteries, and veins. I have experienced it myself. Once I tried a hair gel that gave me such a headache I had to shampoo my hair immediately to get it out.

We need to clear up some of the confusion about the application of natural products to the skin. The skin forms the body's boundary of protection and defense, with millions of soldiers at their stations in the form of skin cells. In my experience, I have observed that the skin is strong, but is actually more vulnerable or receptive to natural substances than to inorganic material. The skin has its own intelligence; it is able to reject, or simply not absorb, the unnatural materials.

When the skin is subjected to incompatible influences such as pollution, the damage to healthy skin will only be external. On the other hand, if "natural" cosmetics are applied frequently to the skin, this permits absorption into the dermal layer, filling up the skin with superfluous substances. Some of the "natural" ingredients go underneath the skin and build up ten times more deposits than were there before. The skin may be an organ, but it is not designed to process like the stomach does; it is completely different tissue with its own functions. The additional elements add weight to the skin, causing it to sag and develop toxicity that can result in sinus problems, nerve damage, and wrinkles.

Marma Creams

Different creams have been developed for the various needs of the body. Marma creams are applied all over the skin, using the appropriate cream for each particular part of the body. The herbal essences in the creams are formulated to benefit specific bodily parts according to their needs and metabolic processes. Each cream complements the effects of the other creams. When used together, the specific herbal combinations of each cream reinforce the complete benefit of the whole.

All the creams can be used for every skin type and can be used by men as well as women. This is possible because the ancient herbal formulas allow the body to balance itself at the source of skin problems, instead of superficially addressing the symptoms at the surface.

The creams which I have developed as a vehicle for the herbal extracts contain **aloe vera** as one of the most important ingredients. Aloe has always worked well as a base and an antiseptic. Aloe is combined with other ingredients in an innocuous blend that gently bonds to the surface of the skin. This blend allows the skin to retain its own moisture and is light enough to contain the live molecular compounds of the herbal ingredients.

The cream base is the plate for the food that feeds the skin. We do not ingest the plate, only the food. In the same way, the special extracts of herbs are energetically compatible with the subtle pathways just beneath the skin. Once the cream is applied, the herbal ingredients stimulate the surface of the skin through the special process of energy resonance. This process is essential in order to generate the proper stimulation of the marmas. The resonance activates currents that connect with the inner aura, bringing out the light and encouraging the body's own rejuvenative abilities. The aura brightens, just as a room fills with sunshine when the windows are opened. The herbal molecules continue to have a lightly stimulating effect all day long.

Basil and saffron have natural antiseptic properties and help to protect against environmental influences and bacterial attack on the skin. That is the reason why basil has been planted right in front of the house for thousands and thousands of years, and why basil and saffron are blended into my herbal formulas. An antiseptic can attack bacteria from the outside before it has a chance to enter the body. There is a similar action in the chemical ingredients which are used for general bacteria prevention after getting cuts or burns.

There are several varieties of basil, and each one has been assigned the name of a deity. The effects of the plants are so well respected that the names of the deities serve as a reminder that remains for the next generation. This in no way interferes with any belief system; it is simply for the purpose of leaving a legacy for the succeeding generations.

I use the meat of the **coconut** in my creams in order to give thickness to the cream, instead of using real butter. When butter becomes old, it spoils very quickly, so I use coconut to keep the creams fresh. The extract of the root of the coconut is also used to give strength to the external part of the skin.

Coconut trees are good for a great many reasons. We call them *kalpa vrisha*, which means every single piece can be used. Coconut water is more wholesome than water and contains many beneficial minerals and vitamins. Coconut meat is equal to butter, and coconut oil is excellent to use for soaps, cooking, and cosmetics. The husk can be used as a spoon. The external part of the coconut can be made into very strong ropes for carpets, rugs, and wall hangings. The wood of the coconut is used to build roofs of houses in certain countries. The leaves of the coconut can be used for roof tiles and can provide an air-conditioned climate within the house.

Some coconuts do not grow to full size, but fall off the tree in different stages. Coconut buds can be used as an excellent remedy for the type of headache that affects the forehead; this headache is caused by discomfort in the intestine. Take the coconut and grind it on a rough surface, put it on the forehead if you have a headache, and you will see the results in just a few minutes. The root of the coconut is used as a medicine for rheumatism or protruding small veins.

The differentiation of the formulas for each of the creams and teas took many long years of research to develop correctly. If there is the slightest deviation from the formula, the desired effects will not follow. The energy technology is in my herbal formulas and also in the medium of a modern cream base. The creams have the right consistency to contain the herbal energy until they are applied to the skin, at which time the cream serves to convey the stimulating essences through the skin. In addition to the energetic stimulation, the herbs have been known to assist the body in throwing off carbon dioxide and absorbing more oxygen.

Cosmetics

Modern cosmetics may have lost the energy component, but the ritual of applying make-up to eyebrows and lips, powders to chin and cheeks, and perfume behind the ear and on the throat, are *all* based on Marma Science. Herbal topicals have existed in every Indian tradition. Indian priests apply different types of herbal paste on various parts of their bodies to cool down their marmas. When people worship in temples, the priest blesses them by placing a small dot of special red paste on their foreheads which stimulates and cools down the 72,000 nerves in the body and balances the mind.

Please see figures 23 and 24 in the center of this book
[Indian Cosmetics]

In India, women used to apply different types of herbs according to the traditions of herbal cosmetics. My sister would make her own natural lipstick. When I asked her why she was doing that, she said, "It is simply to make my lips look healthier." In fact, the lip area is connected to the stomach and intestine. When lipstick made from a natural herbal formulation is applied, it stimulates the stomach and corrects the digestive organs.

How could a little herb stimulate the entire stomach? How can a huge machine start with a single switch? If you think in the modern way, one touch of a little button can operate an enormous machine. A natural herbal formula can act as a small switch of concentrated energy which can activate the channels that connect to the entire stomach area. A pattern of circuitry carries the energy from one point to the other: the energetics of the herbs stimulate the energy centers on the lips, which then activate the subtle channels that connect to and stimulate the stomach. That is why kissing the lips is very stimulating sexually, as are the ears, which are connected to and can stimulate many organs of the body.

Herbs in paste form and herbal treatments have existed for thousands of years and people have used them cosmetically for as long a time. Even during ancient times, there were spas where kings and queens would go for treatments. The reformulation of these herbs into modern creams, without losing any of their qualities or benefits, is a blessing from God. When this ancient method of herbal energetics is followed as it is laid out, we can awaken our life energy, magnetize our charisma, feel happy and more confident, look vibrant and more attractive.

Cellulite

Cellulite is often caused by modern beauty practices. Part of the problem is our own stress, which creates an acidity disorder and accumulates the calcium deposits from different parts of the body which cannot be thrown off by the skin, liver, kidneys, or nails. (Nails are the waste product of the fibers and calcium clearing out of the body.) When the marmas are blocked in the internal part of the body, the flow of the calcium waste also gets blocked. The body has to deposit this waste somewhere, so it stores the waste in the outer part of the leg, the inner part of the thigh, the inner part of the arm or the outer part of the arm. That is one type of cellulite creation.

Another part of the problem is the deposit of extra food we put inside which cannot be utilized by the body and has to be stored somewhere. This extra food goes to the stomach first, then to the hips and near both breasts. Slowly, this stored food spreads out everywhere. It depends on the distribution of extra energy, forming new deposits on top of old.

Another cause of cellulite is modern fashion, such as bikini underwear. Tight elastic around the leg and hip concentrates the fat and cellulite in that area. A woman who wears this clothing all day long is affecting the energy circulation in the area of the thighs and buttocks. Most women's underwear is made to fit right on the hip, where a very important marma is located. The two hip marmas are the exit doors for the fat which is going out of the body. When they get blocked, especially when they are tightly confined all day long, cellulite accumulates.

Once I was working with a woman whose cellulite would not go away. She continually wore extremely tight bikini briefs. Even though I would succeed in breaking down the cellulite, her continued use of briefs caused the cellulite to thicken, causing more blockage. Wearing undergarments that fit a little loosely can improve the circulation.

The cellulite found in the outer and inner thighs has layers. If we were able to break down these layers and look inside, they would look like dry mud. Each of the layers creates a design. Underneath each layer is a very thick concentration of fat, tightened with nerves, veins, and arteries. These are stuck together like the roots of a tree caught underneath a stone. Some of the small veins and capillaries on the legs try to escape, or else they are found lodged between the fat. The nerves and marmas need to be activated to clear the deposits and restore the energy flow.

CHAPTER NINE

Sexual Attraction

Beauty is more than physical; being beautiful and charismatic, looking handsome and attractive, are ultimate manifestations of health and spirituality. This Indian concept of beauty has been a cultural foundation for thousands of years — a complete and deep understanding that beauty begins with the fundamental health of the human body. But health which lacks balance in body, mind, and spirit does not result in real beauty. If there is no real beauty, there is no charisma. If there is no charisma, there is no sexual attraction.

The desire to look good is important as a reflection of physical, mental, and spiritual achievement. No matter what structural type a person may be, there is an energy that can be created from within which will attract a partner of the opposite energy. There is always a connection to be made — an energetic connection to pure energy — when it is created within. The body is not the attraction; it is the subtle energies which attract each other. They have sex together. They have feelings together. Have you ever seen a couple who, individually, are not very physically attractive but soul-wise are very much connected? The reason for that connection is that their subtle energies are attracted. We call this magnetism charisma.

Naturally, the physiological body becomes weaker with age as different parts of the body lose their strength without proper care. In ancient times, this would happen to healthy people only after the age of sixty or sixty-five. Nowadays this is happening at a younger stage. When the body is not functioning in a state of healthy balance, how can it remain youthful?

There are so many claims that tell us how to become younger and more beautiful, but there is no way we can control age.

The fact is that we will always be aging. However, **we can look younger even though we are aging**. We can remain healthy even though we are aging — healthy and beautiful.

Once we understand this concept and embark on a program to clear the electromagnetic circuitry, we can bring ourselves back to radiant health. We can find joy and happiness in our lives at any age. An Indian saying is, "At seventy years, a woman can be as seventeen years old." She has the same feelings as a seventeen-year-old girl, the same physiological and mental feelings. This saying reflects the fact that Indian women take care of their bodies and keep every part functioning properly. Men's bodies are also affected by skin problems, hair loss, and bone disorders. An energy imbalance will also affect their vitality.

What is Vitality?

What, and where, is vitality? Where does the energy come from? In men, it is centered in the solar plexus, where they have the most strength; in women, it is in the heart. Acidic disorders will affect men in the solar plexus. People think stomach disorders or stomach problems are caused by acidity, but it is not that simple. Stress produces bile and acidity which fill up the solar plexus area. Then the heart chakra becomes toxic. Toxicity of the heart chakra affects our emotions. When vitality is compromised, so are our feelings. In order to have a clear energy flow, we need to keep the solar plexus extremely healthy and clean.

We communicate to another person through energy. The heart chakra is one of the most powerful centers. When two people face each other, each has energy coming from more than just the eyes. There are actually two other "eyes" which emit energy: one in the third eye area on the forehead and one in the region of the heart. The eyes, heart, and solar plexus all transmit energy and communicate to the other person. When people meet and shake hands, they are communicating from these centers.

Have you ever noticed that when hugging a person you really like, that hug has a pronounced effect on your physiology and your mind? Touching each other, especially for two people in a relationship, gives each person a very special energy because both the masculine and feminine sides are fulfilled. If both are compatible, the experience has even a stronger effect because each energy connects to the other. This brings a unanimity which stimulates the complementary energies. When hugging, the woman is stimulating the man's heart and solar plexus while the man is stimulating the woman's heart.

When the solar plexus and the heart join together, this creates fire and air. What happens when fire meets air? The attraction causes the flames to grow.

Sexual love is one of the most basic exercises of all. It stimulates the chakras as well as releasing blockages inside the body. When we are in a deep love relationship, a proper relationship, we are naturally stimulating these organs. When we have a partner, we are stimulating our love and stimulating the different sexual organs in our body — basically the endocrine system, which is the spirit. The organs of the endocrine system — the spleen, pancreas, gall bladder, kidneys, adrenal gland, and liver — accomplish incredible work in our body. Love and emotions also stimulate the pituitary gland, which produces hormones.

The Right Partner

When we are not getting proper stimulation with the right partner and the right chemical attraction — even though we may be having sex — we are still not satisfied. That dissatisfaction makes us eat too many sweets and drink coffee because we need somehow to stimulate these organs. That is the way people end up in addictions. Even though they may have very good partners, they may smoke or drink because they are not completely satisfied. They are not stimulated in these specific organs in their body, so they become starved. They crave love.

In Kerala, people have been very careful about creating the right chemistry between a man and a woman. Similar to landscaping the trees and plants around the house for harmony, once a man and woman have decided to have children, the special time for conception is calculated astrologically. When I was a child, an old man told me of a community where people wake up at a specific time of the day or night, shower, light a candle, and make love to create children. The secret is arranging the right chemistry for love. Parents' love for each other creates children born in love. That is the best way for a baby to be born. The month in which the child is born determines the character and its compatibility with the parents' energy.

Most people have heart and skin problems related to their chemistry. Emotionally, we can be attached to someone, but it does not mean we have the right partner. Love means the proper stimulation of the specific physical organs, glands, and nerves in our body. In a relationship, we are stimulating the pituitary gland, thyroid gland, heart, digestive and reproductive organs. Visually, the attraction is focused on the other person's face. When we are visually attracted to this person, we are stimulating the whole brain area, including the pituitary gland. When we are thinking about another person positively, we are stimulating our nerve centers. When we feel very deep emotions towards the other person, when we are kissing him or her on the lips, we are restimulating all the digestive organs.

In this modern world, it is often difficult to find the right chemistry in a partner. Using the herbal creams and teas will stimulate the marmas, which will stimulate life in general and, more specifically, the exchange of love and emotions between partners. Sharing love and emotions is all based on chemical attraction. Marma Skincare keeps a person's energy alive so that one can feel charisma and attraction towards another.

Sometimes when we do not have very compatible chemistry, it will affect the stimulation of our own energies inside. How can we balance that energy even though we might not find the right chemistry with a partner? After years of thought, I created Marma Skincare to balance this chemistry which we are unable to balance through our own sharing.

Misbehaviors, misunderstanding each other, competition with each other are all based on a lack of chemistry. As we know, we can get along with some people while we have trouble getting along with others. In the modern world, we have to adjust to each other. We cannot blame our own lack of stimulation on someone else. Sometimes we try to be alone and lonely rather than trying to balance our chemistry with that of another. **Having a relationship is much more rewarding when we are first in balance within ourselves and when each person has a strong flow of life force that will bring mutual satisfaction.**

We can be fulfilled in many ways — sharing emotions, loving someone, having a good relationship sexually, mentally, physically, or spiritually. It does not matter how. The soul makes us aware of joy, well-being, and the fulfillment of our happiness.

When a client comes for a consultation, I do not do marriage counseling, but I can figure out where the blockages are and how to balance their chemistry. These energy obstacles can happen because of planetary influences, injuries, or any number of other factors. Sometimes it is not only the time of birth, but the release of blockages that is important. Once we know where the energy needs to be stimulated, we figure out a solution.

Solitude is not the same as loneliness. No one has to be lonely. Even though I have seen many people concerned about their physical chemistry, I have also seen many people so improved that they found good partners or renewed their existing love relationship. People who had resigned themselves to being alone turned their life around completely. Partners who had become bored after years together re-ignited the passion of their love. The quality of their energy became much better and they are very happy now.

Sexuality and Spirituality

These days, we do not often think about the ancient teachings of spirituality through sexuality. The ancient people were not ashamed of talking about sex or even enjoying it themselves. There was no shame associated with sex as there is today. The politics of religion have made people feel guilty to the point where they think of sexuality as a bad thing. Actually, the exact opposite is true.

From ancient times, the Indian culture has always been very careful to avoid this complex in children. Even the temples in India were built with sexual depiction to prove that there is no difference between celibacy or non-celibacy for spiritual attainment. The goal is the same; the journey depends on which way we choose to go.

Improving our own chemistry for strength and adaptation is necessary since we are not all born in the most favorable times. I have had consultations with people around the world in various countries where they use astrology as a path to determine planetary effects on humans. I have observed that there are very few partners that really have the right chemistry, who feel a natural attraction. Many astrologers say there are no good matches left because people's energy has become so imbalanced.

Energy channels need to remain open for the life force to flow, so the energy of our body can be protected from any kind of chemistry imbalance. This is the reason for tantric medicine and ancient treatises that discuss spiritual attainment through sexuality. However, this spiritual attainment can only be achieved if we have the right chemistry with our partner. Otherwise, sex can rob the body and mind, causing the opposite effects without giving the benefits. In the same way, incorrect breathing or meditation practices will not wake up the energy that helps us connect to God.

In India, over a thousand years ago, pleasure and sensuality were appreciated as sacred and spiritual. People were well aware of the finer sensibilities and they developed many techniques to enjoy the pleasures of life. They created texts such as the *Kama Sutra*, a primer for sexual intercourse. Each of the positions outlined in the *Kama Sutra* is used to stimulate our marma. Since it is not always easy to find the right chemistry between partners, herbal formulas were developed to correct the chemistry and stimulate pleasurable sensuality of the marma, thus enhancing romantic feelings and gentle affection.

PART THREE

SPIRITUALITY AND BEAUTY

~

CHAPTER TEN

Meditation and Mudras

There is no beauty without spirituality. There is no spirituality without beauty. If we are really spiritual, we look handsome and healthy. That is the way it works. We are comfortable with ourselves and confident with others, secure and absolutely happy in our lives.

A spiritual connection is developed through practices — meditation, proper breathing, proper mudras and mantras, and, basically, praying. It is of the greatest importance to meditate the right way, which necessarily involves learning meditation from a master. The meditation that I teach is one of the most powerful of all. Kalari Meditation (KM) and Nadi Sutra Kriya (NSK) are extremely effective in gaining concentration and augmenting other abilities.

KM is a powerful meditation in Kalaripayat, practiced for concentration and maximum strength before going into the battlefield. People would take a special diet and use this meditation to prepare for fighting. This technique has been adapted for stress reduction of the modern world and is offered in my workshops. NSK is described in this chapter.

The Indian warriors who used this meditation before going to the battlefield kept their minds stabilized and their emotions confident and secure, even in the midst of challenges. It also sharpened their intuition so that with a single look they could identify an enemy.

What is Meditation?

Meditation is the key to everything in our lives. When we sleep, we are not actually resting. Our mind and body are working 24 hours a day, 365 days a year. When we sleep, the mind is busy clearing out everything we have done during the day. There are 72 thousand nerve centers, spread throughout the body, which are stimulated by the marmas and are functioning around the clock, even in deep sleep. The only time they rest is in *dhyana*, or meditation, when the mind achieves deep stillness and union with God — when mind and body finally achieve integration with Spirit. We know how much rest we give to our body; luckily, our minds do not need as much rest. Our minds need only to rest for one or two hours a day. Even half an hour a day will settle the mind and nervous system.

We are already doing activity for the physical body by walking and exercise. When we think, we are working the mind, which is the nervous system. But we also need some exercise for the endocrine system, because that is the dwelling of spirit! That exercise is meditation. Isn't it fair to give attention to our soul for an hour or so every day? Even if we start with only ten or twenty minutes a day, this will enrich our spirituality. This is what meditation is all about — developing the soul. Think of meditation as giving exercise to the soul.

People have such misunderstandings about meditation. Meditation does not exclusively belong to a spiritual community. Meditation is done by every living being on earth. Birds sit and meditate. Monkeys sit and meditate. Every living animal, every living thing, meditates. Even trees and plants meditate in the sense of connecting with universal energy. At higher evolutionary levels, the soul's awareness of spirit is more conscious, and meditation is a matter of concentrating to disengage the mind and reach communion with the divine. We are all spiritual beings who need spiritual practices.

We need to strengthen our endocrine system and develop our Spirit. That means we need to balance ourselves in order to meet with God. The unification of body, mind, and spirit — the integration of these three is our connection to God. Just balancing the body does not eliminate the need for God. We need to connect with God. That is the function of our nature. It is as though we are a computer holding its own electrical cord and we think we do not have to plug it in. We connect to our power supply when we connect with God. Meditation can bring complete rest to the mind and help us achieve the ultimate state of consciousness.

Meditation for Peace of Mind

There are many different forms of meditation, most of them best done properly with the teacher's instructions. This Meditation for Peace of Mind is a simple exercise that can be done by anyone, anytime, anywhere.

Before doing this meditation, take three deep breaths.
• On the first breath, take as much air into the lungs and diaphragm as you normally do, breathing. Breathe out.
• On the second breath, increase the amount of air on the inhalation and then exhale, emptying the lungs and diaphragm.
• Third, take the maximum breath possible as you inhale. Exhale completely. This breath opens up every part of the body.

• Then sit quietly in meditation, continuing a normal breathing, inhaling and exhaling. Let all the thoughts flow out with the exhale. Do not control the mind. There will be a stream of thoughts flowing through from the mind with the third breath. Let all those thoughts come out. In the beginning, you may have surprisingly many thoughts coming out, but after some time, much of the thoughts and negativity will be cleaned out and there will be a reduction of thoughts.

After some time, within two or three months of doing this meditation, we start to feel a sudden silence during the meditation instead of all the thoughts coming out. Later on, your mind starts to see your self. You start to go inside yourself and see . . . your physical self first. Second is your mental figure. Third is your spiritual, or soul, figure. Once you have seen these three levels, you will start to see incredible stillness and emptiness. When you achieve this position, you are in absolute joy and have peaceful feelings.

As you progress through these levels, it is best to do the purification and regular practice of NSK to have maximum benefits. Releasing the blockages also helps to overcome any disturbance. This is one of the most basic meditations. When it is used as a group meditation, it is powerful and each person feels stronger.

The Mirror of God

Some of the temples in India were created by Narayana Guru. He had been a great philosopher and an enlightened master who practiced yoga and meditation for years. Sri Narayana decorated his temples with one mirror. Simply one mirror, that was all. He was saying that if we look at the mirror, we see a god. We see ourselves when we look at the mirror; we see our face and our memories. That means God is in us. I could not understand this at first, but what he was saying was that since God is in us, when we look at ourselves, we see God. God is each one of us.

Years later, when I was practicing meditation, I began to see the phenomenon Narayana Guru had described. While doing meditation, we can actually see incredible changes happening in our body, mind, and spirit. All our emotions start to come out; all our fears start to come out; all our blockages break up. We are able to see our true selves sitting right in front of us and smiling. We can see God inside of ourselves. Once we achieve that position without any blockages, we are fulfilled.

Meditation and the Marmas

Why does fear appear in our bodies? From blockage of the marmas. That is why it is important to meditate correctly. First the body has to be properly prepared in the most profound way by caring for the chakras and energy centers. Only then can we do daily disciplines such as aligning the chakras, opening up the entire marma system, and doing *mudras* (physical practices), *mantras* (sound practices), and *pranayama* (breathing practices).

There are twenty-one marmas that are very powerful. The displaced energy from those marmas can affect specific marmas connected to different organs of the body. This is why people get sick. Many people who have introduced and taught meditation to others are unaware of the marmas. They do not know how to care for the marmas.

Within the body, there is a network of interlaced triangles in which marma blockages can multiply. Obstruction of the energy flow in the marmas is the initial cause of low vitality and imbalances. If there is a spinal cord blockage, the energy does not rise properly; it attacks a marma which is in the center of the spine. That particular marma in the spinal cord is connected to every single part of the body. From that point, many more marmas all over the body can be affected over a period of time. A pattern develops. It takes weeks, months, or years for different blockages to reach different marma points, depending on the original point of the injury. Marma specialists are able to see exactly when the blockage began. They can know what caused it, how it started, and how long it has been there.

The proper way of meditation strengthens the marmas. Shiva, Lord of Yogis, is the only one who knows all the 840 million marmas, as well as the 840 million yoga postures, learned from the 840 million life forms on earth. Such profound wisdom has great compassion. These patterns of marmas and postures are the blueprint to help people unblock and cleanse their energy channels.

Rising Energy

When we meditate, we are lifting the energy from the bottom of the hip area, the *muladhara* (lower chakra), to the upper part of the head. In this pattern from bottom to top, there are many interconnected energies among the marmas and the chakras.

Please turn to figure 25 in the center of this book
[Chakras and marmas]

The patterns of energy rising up the body can be compared to a winter's road trip. Driving a car on a snowy road, the car can slip here and there; wherever there is a slope, the car can go over the edge. No matter how we may try to control the car, it will slip and go over. The same is true when the energy pathways in the body are not clear. When we start to lift the energy it begins to move, but where can it go? If there is a blockage in any area, the passage is obstructed, and the energy is diverted.

In another comparison, raising the energy is like pumping a viscous liquid through a pipe. Naturally, it is very difficult to move this liquid, so we pump with great force. If there is a hole anywhere in the pipe, the liquid will leak out throught the hole. This liquid is not supposed to leak into places outside its channel, and it is not supposed to drop down. Similarly, the energy in our body can leak and attack the marma channels.

The Body/Mind/Spirit Connection

All the ancient sciences are learned from unadulterated, original traditions. People who practice the right way of thought – learned from a master with a soul foundation – carry the integrity of the tradition. The effects of correct meditation will be a compassionate nature, a positive attitude, and tremendous energy. Practicing the wrong way only takes us further away from natural laws and positive results.

This does not mean that spiritual practices are only for certain people, or that only a select group of humans are truly spiritual. Everyone must connect with the source of life in order to fulfill his or her life's purpose. However, attempting to do so without first cleansing and purifying the system can produce negative results. The meditation practices I teach are the result of many years of personal development and research to locate the real means of enlightenment, without missing any links in the chain.

The ancient yogis used to take scrupulous care of their bodies because they knew that Spirit develops from a fully functioning physiology. The body is very precious for spiritual awareness. Depending on what we want in life and which part of the body needs to be stimulated or relaxed, we choose the method we want to use — mantras, mudras, pranayama, or a combination of these techniques. Spiritual practices are like cuisine. We can be creative, using different food groups to prepare a delicious meal. Likewise, we can take something from each of the different spiritual disciplines.

In meditation, we use our will and concentration to re-create our connection with Spirit. Whatever thoughts may come are the waste products of the mind, so we let thoughts come out and let them go. After some time there are no thoughts, only emptiness.

During meditation, one may start to see the colors of the different chakras and experience the qualities of the chakras. That is a marvelous feeling. Meditating in water can be particularly effective. There is a powerful meditation taught in my practice where the search for enlightenment is done systematically, helping one achieve tremendous power and

CENTER FOR HEALTH AND EVOLUTION

CREATION OF THE SAFEST AND MOST BEAUTIFUL PLACE ON EARTH

[A non-profit center dedicated to preserving the most sophisticated ancient knowledge and providing the best technology of rejuvenation and health care for everyone.]

PHILOSOPHY

It is my intention to preserve the world's most precious technology of destiny-fulfilling knowledge for present and future generations. As it is an empirical system of knowledge with a very practical spirituality, the best preservation would be to create the safest place on earth. Safe from all the stress of modern life and planetary disruptions, the harmonizing energy and treatments there would embody a pure, thorough, and profound integration of body and soul. This place of refuge would instill a feeling of security in knowing that you will be taken care of in the most effective and natural ways possible.

This is the philosophy of the Center for Health and Evolution. Being healthy means fulfilling every desire in every cell in the body. Health means much more than fixing the bone or the pain in the body; it is a positive existence. Being spiritual means every cell in your body resonates with the desire to fully connect with God. One can work on the integration of the desires of all three dimensions — physical, mental, and spiritual - in the Center. We can know the different aspects of ourselves and learn that life can be glorious.

The wisdom for attaining a life of healthy comfort and evolved consciousness has existed for 12,000 years in India. When I was a boy, my teacher once took me to see a village of enlightened people. Although we approached at night, the secluded village was bright with a luminous glow. This was not artificial light. It was the natural light of a group of people functioning at a high level of consciousness, producing a collective brilliance. I remember this light as having an ethereal beauty and sensed a powerful protection surrounding the village.

FUNCTION

There are very sophisticated methods and guidelines for physical, mental, and spiritual balancing. Allow me to describe some aspects of the sanctuary that I envision.

Upon entering this place, one can feel the healing vibration in the atmosphere. There is a vibrational field of balanced electromagnetism, which has some incredible effects on the mind, inducing a more positive perspective. This technology is based on the original energy medicine, which delineates the structure and relationships of universal energy in terms of human beings and their environment. The environment is more than our immediate surroundings - it extends beyond the galaxy and includes the planetary influences.

Now that the ozone layer no longer has its normal, protective, filtering capacity, both positive and negative planetary influences enter the earth's atmosphere to a greater degree than before. The life-preserving advantage of being in an area of balanced electromagnetic energy is that the negative influences are dissipated and the positive influences are absorbed.

One of the methods used to accomplish this energy balance is the use of certain herbal combinations that change the chemistry of the atmosphere, bringing all the positive frequencies of the universe into alignment. That positive energy can influence the surrounding environment to create an atmosphere of happiness, joy, and love among people.

There is a delicate balance in human chemistry that is influenced by environmental effects in daily life. Society is organized in such a way as to slow the wheels of evolution, but in changing ourselves, we have the ability to bring harmony everywhere.

To accomplish this, we need the most positive place on earth. All the elements necessary to fulfill human desire are incorporated into the arrangement, with the implicit understanding that nothing is ever forced on anyone. Fulfillment of desire needs to be discreet in the sense that, in the absence of force, our mind will surrender. Then we can use the mind for our needs, rather than letting the mind control us. The natural order is soul over mind, mind over body.

There is a very well-calculated system that has been used in the world by our ancestors in creating the environment to please the mind. When the mind becomes aware, it resists. What we can do is intelligently feed every desire until the mind surrenders. We can let it have everything it wants without any force being used or harm being done. I have applied this "non-force" technology over the past twenty years and realized that it is most effective. Non-aggression works at a very practical level.

Most disease is created from the mind controlling the body. People are learning that psychology and biology are overlapping sciences. Emotions follow thoughts and unexpressed emotion is an energy blockage that needs to be released. Pent-up over time, the damage shows in the physical body. With the proper understanding, a person's mind can fulfill its desires, and, once satisfied, the mind lets go. The rhythm of life is restored as energy circulates through the whole being.

In the center of safety, which is truly a sacred place of transformation, no one tries to cure another person or even guide another. Each person is responsible for her/himself to feed the mind. The most tasteful food is there. People have it when they need it. Everyone goes through a systematic pathway of treatment places where they are able to do for themselves and naturally grow beyond limiting patterns.

One of the specialties of this Center is that people have the option of undertaking programs on their own or choose to have customized treatments administered to them. Training sessions are integral to learn the concepts and methodology. After that, whenever the time seems right, the person goes to a place where there is complete freedom and privacy. There is a systematic way of designing the structure, both physically and energetically, to support and strengthen the practices of growth, awareness, and self-mastery. Virtual reality pales in comparison to real life at its best.

DESIGN

One side of the center is dedicated to spirituality and one side is for enjoyment - the pleasure of body and mind. Desires satisfied in the right way are released. People have the option of choosing either side or both. The most important thing is that fulfilling all aspects can achieve real satisfaction in life.

The two sides of the Center for Health and Evolution is composed represent the dual sides of our own nature. One side is called Spiritual Fulfillment Center and the other is Rejuvenation and Fulfillment of Desires.

As human beings, we all have a longing to be spiritual and a need to fulfill desires. Some people are born with the desire of fulfilling the spiritual side of them. Some want to fulfill all their desires in material, mental, physical, and sexual ways. One can choose either the completion of desires for spiritual callings or the fulfillment of pleasure and enjoyment and, after that, go fully to the spiritual side.

The spiritual practices are based on the clear sciences, very basic sciences of repairing ourselves — physically, mentally, spiritually - and connecting to God without depending on any mediators. Following the system of exercises and practices takes us where we need to go. It is like having a clear, detailed map. Most significantly, there is complete freedom in reaching the destination.

SUBTERRANEAN CENTER

Most of the treatments are done underground at the Center for Health and Evolution. We all try to get away from outside stress, but we do not think about the stress coming from the outer planets. Some of the rejuvenation done underground specifically prevents the undesirable energy coming from the interplanetary sources.

Twelve different treatment systems are available in the Subterranean Center, sufficient for general rejuvenation of the whole body, mind, and spirit. The underground treatments can be done separately to restore the energy system of the body. Other more specific or advanced cases of illness are given very special care and attention with customized treatments. People who cannot afford to have the treatments will be funded from donations. In this way, everyone can be rejuvenated.

SPIRITUAL GEOMETRY

Our planet is influenced by other planets and the stars. For each person born, there is a group of stars born, taking position in the galaxy according to the exact position in our body. In this regard, the healing can be customized for each and every person. These custom designs send the light energy to our body as well as the surroundings, including house, trees . . . everything surrounding us.

The correspondence of lights between God stars and ourselves must be kept very clear. Missing that correspondence can lose the messages of fortune, blessings, joy, and happiness. There is a shift in the patterns of communication four times annually, or every three months in the calendar year of twelve months. At these junctures, the changes of light have to be received very carefully.

Light brings clarity. We need many lights to brighten one area, although a particular light can brighten even large surroundings, having an effect on everyone. Lights enter our planetary field through eight corners on the earth, multiplying 8 x 8 to reach 64 areas on earth. In these sixty-four areas, we can attract the light energy, store it, and distribute it through everyone to cover our planet.

I have worked with the principles of the sixty-four different energy locations in the body where illness begins. There are eight main corners which, when squared, equals sixty-four. As I said in Chapter Five, the earth functions with the same principles of universal law as those of the human body. With these principles, we can also preserve the earth by multiplying the same system into eight main centers. From there, it expands to sixty-four branch centers. This network will cover the planet and is the basis of the universal principles of the energy system.

Based on this philosophy of the Center for Health and

Evolution, this system will cover all the requirements of human needs. We are simultaneously preserving the most fundamental and the most powerful of all sciences, centralized in one place, for ourselves and the future generations to be awakened. The most advanced technology of health and rejuvenation will be preserved in the United States forever.

We can create a bioelectric circuitry that connects the universal mind and amplifies the natural light everywhere. Everyone going through the sanctuary derives the benefits of the energy there, enjoying the beauty of the lights and absorbing the positive qualities that guide us to the right path. Understanding of other people blossoms from the heart, bringing with it the happiness and joy of harmonious vibrations.

Figure A   The Center for Health and Evolution

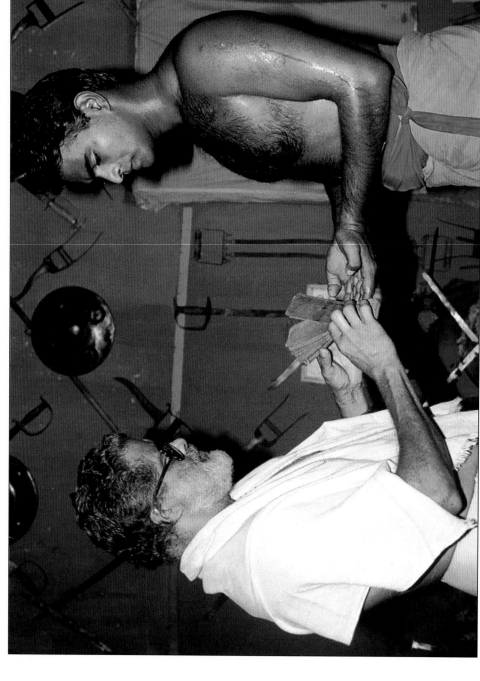

Figure 1   *Master passing herbal formulas to Joseph Kurian*

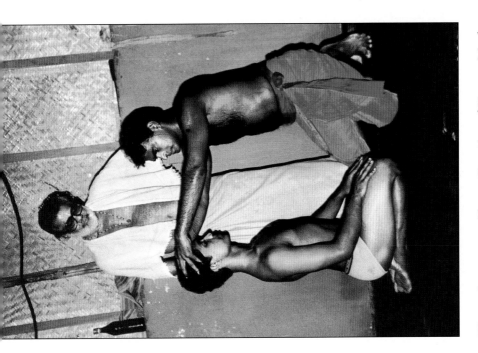

Figure 2   *Above: Practice of Veerya Mudra, special breathing technique to strengthen internal power*

Figure 3   *Below: Master teaching Joseph Kurian the secret of Nadi Sutra, a nerve stimulation technique*

Kalaripayat develops strength and flexibility from an intimate awareness of the energy system (figures 4-10).

Figure 4

Sword fight with Joseph Kurian avoiding attack by jumping high in the air

Figure 5
Figure 5.5

Left: Joseph Kurian demonstrating defensive posture in Kalaripayat
Right: Joseph Kurian in the jumping posture of Kalaripayat

Figure 6
Figure 6.5

Left: One variety of Otta fight movement
Right: Joseph Kurian showing Kalaripayat "throwing" technique

Figure 7   *Above: Joseph Kurian with Master practicing hand lock with a weapon called "Otta"*
Figure 8   *Below: Otta fight– Joseph Kurian and partner in one of several beautiful, rhythmic jumping movements*

Figure 9   *Deadly lock position*
Figure 10   *Kalaripayat flying technique in Parisian stadium*

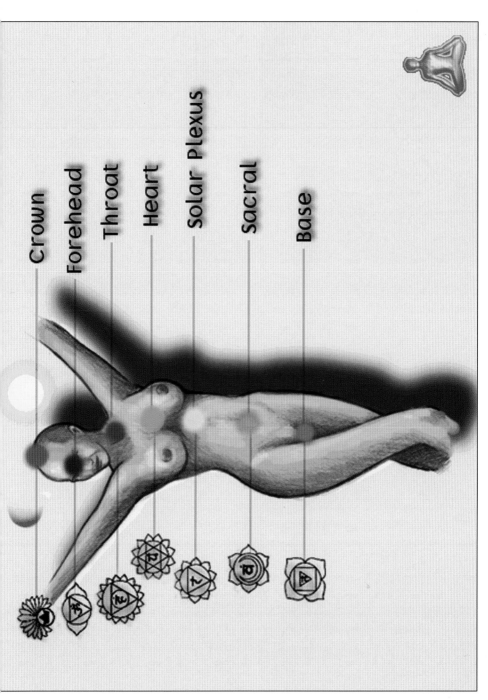

Crown

Forehead

Throat

Heart

Solar Plexus

Sacral

Base

Location of seven chakras on the body

Figure 11

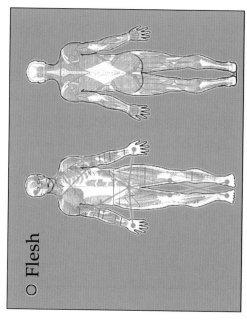

Arteries

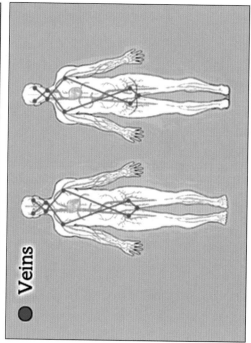

○ Flesh

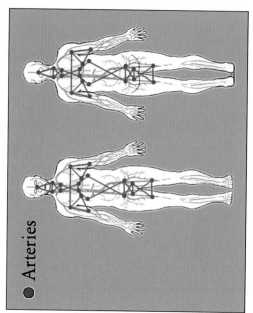

● Arteries
● Veins
○ Flesh
○ Lymph System
● Joints
● Bones
● Nerves

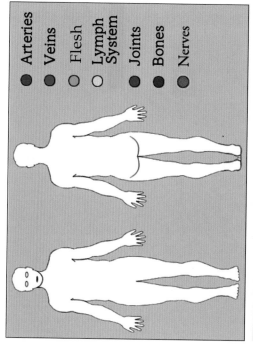

● Veins

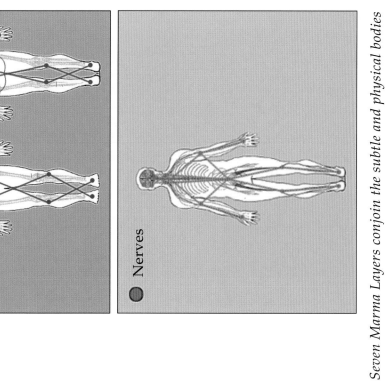

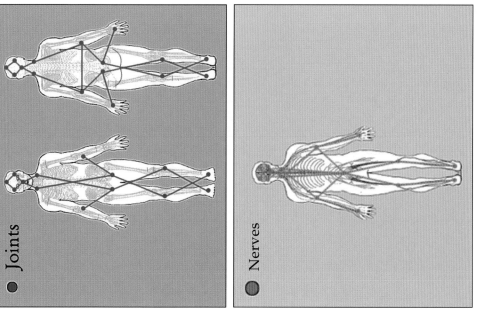

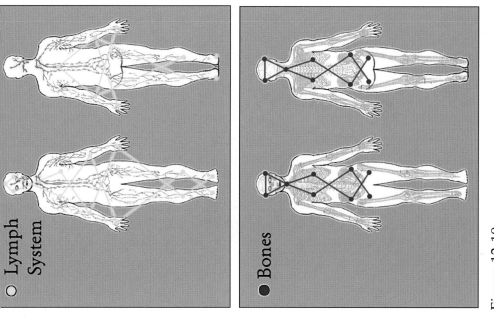

○ Lymph System

● Joints

● Bones

◉ Nerves

Seven Marma Layers conjoin the subtle and physical bodies

Figure 12-19

Written formulas preserved on palm leaf scrolls

Figure 20 and 21

Figure 22   *Precise blends of herbs create new synergy*

Figure 23 and 24

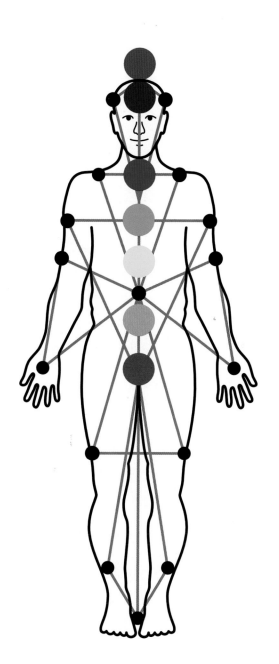

Energy rises up the chakras and is distributed throughout the system

Figure 25

Figure 26

Energy is transposed through seven levels of body, mind, and spirit

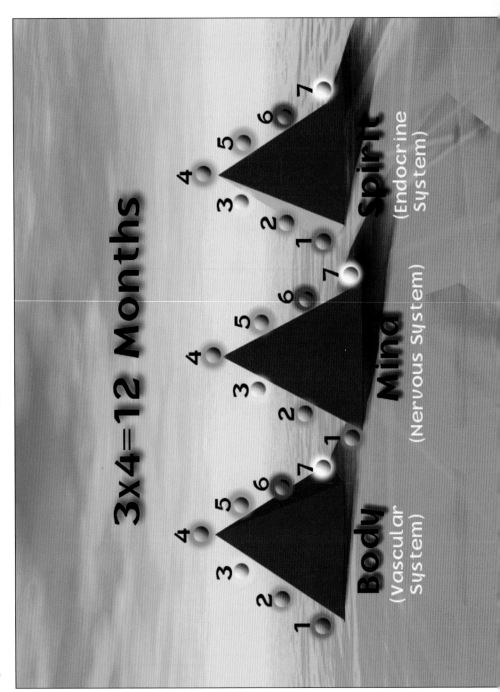

Herbs mixed with gems absorb solar and planetary energies

Figure 27

Figures 28, left: H.H. The Maharaja of Panna from Vanishing India by Stowitts, 1929
Figure 29, right: His Exalted Highness Nizam II Mulk Asaf Jah of Hyderabad from Vanishing India by Stowitts, 1929
                   Both are Courtesy of The Stowitts Museum and Library, www.stowitts.org

*Figure 30 H.R.H. The Maharaja of Gidhour in Bengal from Vanishing India by Stowitts, 1930
Courtesy of The Stowitts Museum and Library, www.stowitts.org*

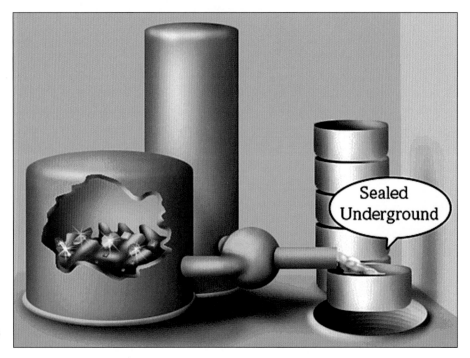

Esoteric process of transmuting gemstone energy into vibrational essence

Figures 31 and 32

Above: Marma Teas
Below: Marma Skincare

Figures 33
Figure 34

energy in life. These practices are very serious and must be done only through the instruction of the master.

We cannot think positively when our physiology is full of toxins; therefore, I have created many different cleansing and rejuvenating practices in my program. Keeping negative mentality inside never benefits meditation. I recommend that a meditator look into the negative side of the mind and enjoy it with a positive attitude. Meditators can reverse a negative attitude after realizing how much energy it takes to block the natural flow of vitality. When we are positive, our energy level goes up because none of the energy is being diverted.

Mudras

Organs in different parts of the body each have a key for opening up that area — a simple procedure called *mudra*. **A mudra is a movement or posture that connects energy points to complete a circuit, facilitating the flow of life force.** The vital energy is then able to circulate to areas that were previously out of reach. Imagine opening a door for someone who is carrying a weight. In a similar fashion, there are places in the human body that are either blocked or do not open naturally, so help is needed to open up that specific door.

Mudras can be a lifetime study. Mudras, or postures, can be seen in twelve thousand year-old statues in India. Every mudra has its own meaning. The interpretations of these mudras are kept strictly secret, not because the masters are selfish but because they know that if the practice is done incorrectly, the consequences are difficult to correct. Mudras have the power to open up the channels in the body which have a connection to the soul and spirit. Some mudras, in fact, go into the deepest layers of our consciousness. When a specific area is opened up which corresponds to the consciousness, another energy, such as that provided by mantra, needs to enter inside. The use of mantras will be discussed fully in Chapter 11.

Mudras and mantras are all based on brain activity, which is the basis of the integrated circuitry in the energy field. There is no separation between the brain and the body. Mudras are the key for getting the information into the different organs of the body. For that purpose, different fingers are positioned in such a way as to open up the channels of the marmas located in the primary organs. Even the simple act of making the sign of the cross stimulates certain marmas to prepare the mind for expanded awareness.

Stimulating the Heart Marmas

In India, there is a reason for each and every movement. When both palms are pressed together, an energy is created between the hands. When the center of the palms are held toward the heart marma, located on the chest between the nipples, a special energy is created which stimulates the marmas that are connected to the lungs, heart, and emotions.

Stimulating the heart chakra enlivens the entire chakra system and helps to balance the digestive organs. A very common greeting in India is to put both palms together and press them against the chest so that the palms are somewhat open and the thumbs are touching the chest. That specific position of holding the arms and pressing the palms together corrects the lungs. Interestingly, the position of the hands exactly imitates the shape of the lungs.

Hands cupped in bowing position

By holding that position, the lungs are opened so the breath goes equally to every single part of the body, improving circulation. When circulation is in a normal condition, the body is balanced.

Vata, pitta, and kapha are balanced. Air, fire, and water are equally balanced. All the marmas get stimulated in the body. In a balanced situation, one can project happiness to other people and perceive it in them.

Other Mudras

The key to our own bodies, our own souls, is right at our fingertips. Our five fingers correspond to the five primary organs of the body, which are the brain, lungs, intestines, kidneys, and heart. By touching each of the fingers in a specific way, we can open the channels to the individual organs. The organs are directly connected to these *mahamarmas*, which are stimulating the five elements.

Lung Mudra

LUNG MUDRA: Touching the thumb and forefinger together on each hand opens up the lungs and brain. Someone who has problems with asthma or difficulty breathing after exercise, or even someone running long distance, would find this mudra useful to regulate the flow of the breath into the lungs.

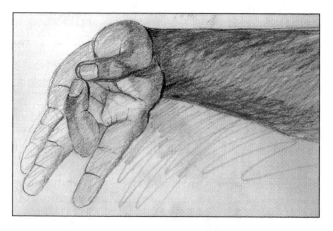

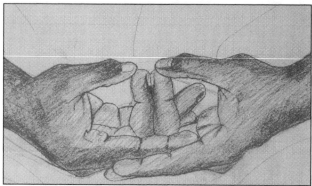

Nerve Mudra

NERVE MUDRA: If an upsetting situation, interview or other important occasion provokes anxiety, touch the middle finger and thumb together on each hand, with the tips of both thumbs touching. In this position, bring the hands about four fingers below the navel and rest the outside of the palms there. Do not worry about getting the exact location because the nabhi marma is as big as the palm of your hand. Hold this position for two or three minutes, eyes closed, and take deep breaths. When finished, go into the Indian bowing mudra. Put both arms together and bring the sides of the palms to the chest. It is also good to do the Marma Mantra for strengthening the mind. Repeat the mantra sound four times.

Kidney Mudra

KIDNEY MUDRA: The kidneys are the key to a strong heart. When the kidneys fill up with toxins, or when they are weak, we become tired. This is because the job of the kidneys is to eliminate water from the body. When the body fills up with water, the muscles and tissues become inflamed. Stress causes most cases of kidney blockage and creates chronic anxiety syndrome. To get quick energy immediately, instead of taking medicine, touch the ring finger and thumb together — a mudra that stimulates the kidneys. Think of the symbolism of the ring finger for marriage — plenty of energy is needed to start a married life.

Heart Mudra

HEART MUDRA: Emotions can be lightly balanced by touching together the thumb and small finger. The little finger corresponds to the heart, and this mudra wakes up the heart marma. Our heart is responsible for circulating the blood all over the body, so it needs stimulation often. But our heart also connects to our emotions and sexual area. Hugging certain people can stimulate the heart chakra very quickly. It all depends on the mutual chemistry, but we can stimulate ourselves with the heart mudra. This simple technique is appropriate when we have an emotional problem or rapid heartbeat from anxiety. Along with the mudra, you could say the Marma Mantra about five times. This combination has helped many people as well as myself.

Mahamudra or NSK (Nadi Sutra Kriya)

The *Nadraja statue* represents a vigorous movement which was first mentioned two thousand years ago when *Kannuadha Maharshi* divided the atom. It has been said that when we divide the atom, the pattern of the particles becomes the *Nadraja statue*. The shape of the following motions is a re-creation of the shape of the statue of the god of knowledge or education.

This exercise may seem simple, but its power is tremendous. I have been practicing this technique for the past twenty-two years and have seen its miraculous effects. The goal is to achieve both the proper experience and complete understanding of the process. Observed carefully, this exercise is symbolic of every Indian spiritual aspect.

The NSK meditation is a *mahamudra*, or great mudra. A combination of simple exercise movements, it includes stimulation of the breathing and chakras. The importance of mudras is the energy connection created in the deeper levels of the body that we may otherwise never stimulate. The particular muscles involved in this mahamudra are connected to very sensitive parts of the internal organs, which are, in turn, connected to the spiritual part of the mind. The correct postures and movements directly exercise these areas.

Practicing the NSK energizes the atomic and molecular levels of our being, which restimulates the electromagnetic field and creates the aura. After the exercise, this expanded field continues as protection. Stimulating this powerful chakra system creates a strong energy field and activates the energy within. Each chakra has a unique, important responsibility. Each is connected to body, mind, and spirit. While doing this meditation, one immediately starts to see how energy comes to the eyes, comes to the body. A wonderful, vibrant feeling, both inside and outside, is the result of finishing this very simple exercise.

Do this practice with great care and the utmost respect for all the organs of your body and every single spiritual aspect inside you. It is the key to connecting with God's energy, which is the spiritual aspect of this exercise. There are also physical benefits, as you will see when you are sitting in position. **Do the NSK no more than three or four times a day.**

You can sit in any comfortable position to do this practice. An added benefit is that you will feel much more comfortable and self-confident, without the withdrawal symptoms and subsequent drop in energy that occur after taking artificial stimulants.

In everyday life, this exercise can be done first thing in the morning; it will supply enough energy for the rest of the day. If the day is busy, recharge your body by doing this simple exercise in the afternoon. After driving for a long time, get out of the car and do this movement. Never do this movement casually or as a public display; it requires the proper respect. Do it in the forest, where there is more oxygen available, or wherever there is a quiet, calm environment.

Most stress is concentrated in the shoulders. The cervical vertebrae marrow is connected to the chakra system on the chest and to the three main chakras, which are directly stimulated by doing this first movement meditation.

Meditating with the mudra for lungs will also help circulate the electromagnetic flow through the nervous system. If you need extra-strong stimulation, you could repeat the Marma Mantra three or four times. This could be a solution for common blockages of the nose.

For sinus or nasal congestion, touch the thumb and forefinger together. If the left nostril is closed, touch the thumb and forefinger on the right hand together. Reverse the procedure to clear the right nostril.

Origin of the NSK Movement

The techniques of NSK originated from methods used by Indian warriors in preparation for the battlefield. Based on deep knowledge of where the sensitive energy centers are located within the body and how to stimulate them, the purpose is to awaken vital energy and courage. Not only the body and mind, but the whole chakra system is opened to generate spiritual well-being and willpower. Energy from the chakras is brought out through interconnecting channels to the outside of the body, where it forms a protective shield.

Equally effective in contemporary life, NSK provides a secret weapon for the challenges of stress and time constraints. The NSK is a remarkably efficient exercise that requires only a few minutes each day to assimilate and balance life force.

NSK Instructions

1) Place hands on opposite knees or calves and breathe deeply. Continue breathing deeply throughout the exercise.

2) Stretch arms in a sweeping motion outward to 90-degree angles from the ground. As the hands sweep upward, the palms face up.

3) Bring the hands behind the head, placing them on each side where the neck meets the shoulders.

4) Open the arms to both sides of the body, with hands raised upward.

5) Bring the arms down, facing palms of the hands together, to the groin area.

6) With fingers pointed downward, massage the chakra system by moving hands all the way upward from the groin to the heart chakra. Then reverse direction of fingetips to point upward. All the energy that has been gathered up as the movement sweeps around is now brought to the heart chakra.

7) Extend the arms in front of the body, leaving the thumbs and little fingers joined together. This is a motion to throw out the impurities gathered by the energy flow of the hand movements.

8) Bring hands, palms facing together, to the point between the eyebrows.

9) Lower the hands in the same position to the heart and hold there, bringing positive energy back into the system.

Repeat the whole exercise four times. When the exercise is performed correctly, it is one continuous, flowing motion.

CHAPTER ELEVEN

Mantras and Pranayama

Mantras are sounds which set up sympathetic vibrations in different marmas of the human body. The repetition of sound has a vibrational effect on the marmas, externally and internally. Each specific word has a resonance. Spirit creates a vibration that resonates with a certain area of the body and moves through the marma channels to reach there.

Mantras are like water. When we touch water, we see the rippling motion of the waves. When we create certain vibrational sounds, those sounds travel along the energy paths which are opened up by the mantras. The sound opens and brings life energy into these paths; it brings the electromagnetic current to a specific area.

Sound in general influences physiology, which is a living resonator for sound. We know that the atom is both wave and particle, subject to different frequencies. Sound has a vibratory rate that carries through subatomic levels, influencing all the layers of the body. The sounds of mantras are carefully calculated to raise the vibrational frequency of the electromagnetic field, or aura. Mantras bring the finer vibrations that satisfy the soul.

OM Mantras

OM appears to be one sound, but it has endless meaning. OM actually contains three sounds, which stimulate lower, middle, and upper chakras. When we say OM, we are saying ah - oo - ma, three sounds which balance the three mahamarmas and which control, respectively, the endocrine, vascular, and nervous systems. When OM divides into ah - oo - ma, the sound stimulates the nervous system, where the nerves converge in the navel area, the chest, where emotions are centralized, and the forehead, where the pituitary gland is located. These three systems correspond to the Ayur Vedic doshas of fire, air, and water.

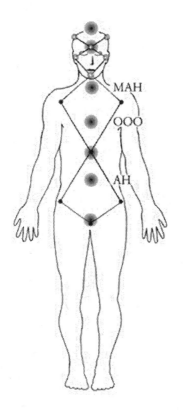

When we say *OM* in a resonant voice, we stimulate the fire, air, and water elements and the endocrine, nervous, and vascular systems. Repeating the OM mantra even three times provides a connection to the universal energy, which gives us light inside and out.

These three centers are interconnected with the other chakras. When we say the mantra *Om Nama Shivaya* (every word in the world is combined into the five words of this mahamantra), we are affecting the five elements, which are the five organs of the body: brain, lungs, intestines, kidneys, and heart. When we repeat this sound, we stimulate the three doshas and the five elements. The sound travels through layer after layer of the body as if they were gossamer veils. As we balance our spiritual manifestation with both physical and subtle bodies, the marmas again play a key role in the conduction of mantras.

Everything in the universe has a frequency. In this ocean of energy, we can choose to be merely a tuning fork responding to a small range of notes, or a finely tuned musical instrument that is one and the same with the celestial song. There is a legend in the East about the soul entering the body for the first time. After God had fashioned a body of clay, the soul was very reluctant to enter it until the angels played celestial music. The sound was so enchanting that the soul went into the body in order to better hear the music.

All sound reverberates within us: every animal sound, natural sound, musical sound. Indian music creates vibrations of the five elements of the universe. The science of music was actually derived from the science of astrology, putting the cosmic vibrations into mathematical arrangements. Every note corresponds to a certain planet and also a particular animal sound. The *ragas* of Indian music are specially composed to have healing and elevating effects.

The sounds of the ancient Sanskrit language are intrinsically uplifting. The traditional languages of India are all designed to stimulate the chakras and speaking them is itself a mantra. Even the act of writing the scriptures is powerful. The symbolic movement of writing the letters is reenacted when I am working on people. The gestures assist in the energy transformation. The Sanskrit language, both written and articulated, is the basis of healing.

The secret code of my work is my own language — the 56-letter *Malayalam* language of Kerala — which is closely related to Sanskrit. When I was a child, my teacher would hold my head and write *Om Nama Shivaya* on my head. I would present him with one gallon of pure rice, which would be placed on the floor. Then my guru would sit in the lotus posture and put me on his leg, take my right hand and ask me to point my index finger to the floor to write, *Om Hare Sri Nama Ha. Om Hare Sri.* We say *Hare* is the guru of writing. So it means, "I respect you, my great guru of education." That purely Indian phrase is the first lesson in writing.

There was nothing more pleasurable in the world than sitting on the lap of my guru as he took my hand and pointed it at the floor to write. That marvelous, wonderful feeling will always be in my heart. Wherever I go, I will remember my guru and the strength which radiated from his chest to the back of my chakras.

Marma Mantra

A basic mantra which can be used every day to stimulate the organs is *Marma*, pronounced *Mmaarrmmaa*. It is important to learn how to pronounce it properly. The ma - rr - ma sounds are deeply connected to the chakras and physiology. By itself, only three times are necessary if we are repeating it very slowly with prolonged pronunciation, as in *mmmmmaaaaarrrrrmmmmmmaaaaa*. Otherwise, eight times a day is enough especially if done in combination with mudras. Even after a few repetitions of the Marma Mantra, we can already start to feel an incredible vibration going through each of the halls of our body.

Marma is a very ancient word, considered to be the pathway to God or the doorstep to Heaven. It has always been highly respected by the great masters of Dhanur Veda, who knew the meaning of marma. The marma sound itself brings success and creativity. Repeating it stimulates the ah - oo - ma, and the third chakra, which is the key to success. Saying that word is itself a perfectly balanced mantra. The Marma Mantra stimulates four aspects of our chakras at once, which cover the three mahamarmas and the marma which generates self- confidence.

Such a word creates inner strength. When people are not strong, they are frightened when they hear the rr - oo - ah sounds. To say marma combines these sounds. "R" is a powerful sound which stimulates the third chakra, the power center where we have the potential for talent and ability. Subtle energies are transmuted into physical, and vital life force is distributed throughout the body. People get excited when they hear *marma*, or are surprised when their blockages are affected in the area of the third chakra. With the Marma Mantra, we concentrate on general awakening, fighting insecurity, and achieving success and self-confidence.

When mantras are repeated along with mudras, a door opens to great benefits. At first, when we do mudras, we slowly start to enter a tunnel which has no end. When we go through that tunnel, we can see golden light and golden doors opening up. We can see the largest treasures in the world and experience the happiness and wealth we need. I have experienced incredible happiness while doing sound practice. Mantras have the power to penetrate the layers of desires in our human body, mind, and spirit, in order to reveal our spiritual side.

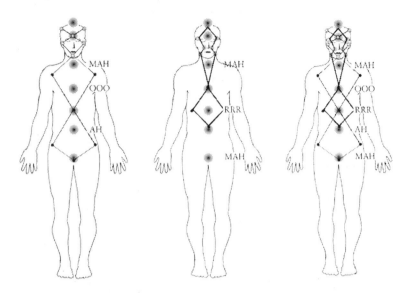

Story of Siddhi

One of the people who worked on our family plantation introduced me to his grandfather, a neighbor of ours, who was extremely accomplished in the practice of mantras. My parents and family thought he was a strange fellow. Still, I was curious about this man. (He turned out to be a very kind, nice person once I got to know him.) In fact, he was born a Christian and had gone somewhere to study for the *siddhi* (mantric power).

One day, I was on our land looking after the coconuts and taking care of the goats when I saw this man coming along the way. He looked in my direction. Since I had been given the energy by the master, he probably recognized it in me, even though I did not know it. That day, the place was totally empty except for the deliveries from steamboats going down the river along our eight acres of rubber plantation. At the time, there was a flood and it was raining slightly. I was taking a delivery from a ship when I looked up and saw this man standing on top of a big stone.

Suddenly the rain stopped. He pointed his stick towards the coconut tree. There were at least a dozen coconuts on the tree. The entire group of coconuts dropped all at once down to the base of the tree. After that, he looked at me with a sidelong glance, smiled, and then just disappeared without even talking to me. I was bewildered and so scared I could hardly move. I wondered, "How could he possibly do that?"

That siddhi was one of the powers of mantra he was showing me. He had completed millions of mantra repetitions. In order to achieve a certain level of power through a mantra, one has to repeat it hundreds of thousands of times so the vibration that occurs in the body will stimulate the kundalini through the chakras. One can attain enormous power from mantra, which can be utilized either for good things such as healing, or can sometimes be misused. Depending on the intention, a person can earn a good life the next time around or have many difficulties in this one. This man tended to use the siddhi in playfulness, which is not the purest motive.

Pranayama

The act of breathing air is more than simply a chemical process of absorbing oxygen and getting rid of carbon dioxide. In the Vedic sciences, breath is known as *prana* — the basis of life. Without prana there are no marmas. Without the marmas, prana cannot be utilized by the human body. Breathing practices make one physically strong, mentally secure and immune to illness. Pranayama stabilizes the psychology and emotions by opening the blockages in the marma channels which correspond to the emotions and by releasing deep sources of insecurity, fear, anxiety, and mental confusion.

Breath must be taken in through the nose in order to be purified. Otherwise, the air we take in builds up dust or chemical pollutants, blocking the marmas and creating bronchial problems in the chest. The sinuses have many ways of removing these foreign elements. One such way is sneezing. It is important never to block these cleansing processes.

The whole idea of breathing is to absorb pranic energy from cosmic energy. That energy is in the air we breathe. As we breathe, 80 percent of the air we take in goes to the lungs to supply the blood with oxygen for the cells, and 20 percent goes to the brain after being purified by the sinuses. Everyone knows we have a stomach which digests food for the body; the sinuses are the stomach which digests food for the mind. The functioning of the brain depends on the ability of the sinuses to purify the breath.

Just as it is important to eat healthy food so that the stomach can easily purify it for its uses in the body, it is equally important to inhale clean air for the sinuses. Breathing polluted air is like eating toxified food. Just as we have ways to purify food before it is eaten, we have ways to purify the air. There are special herbal remedies that are helpful for this such as incense, *puja dravyam, and homas dravyam* (see Chapter 12).

The purified breath is transformed from cosmic energy into pranic energy and then into an electromagnetic current by the hemispheres of the brain surrounding the cerebral cortex. Electricity from the brain and the prana in the breath create an electromagnetic current or aura. The bone marrow is also a key to the strength of the aura and is interconnected with the chakras of the body. When the bone marrow is not clean and clear, intelligence will be adversely affected because the brain is fed the electromagnetic current by the bone marrow. This electromagnetic current is what stimulates the marmas that control the functions of the entire body.

It is well understood that we use a very small percentage of the electromagnetic potential of the hemispheres of the brain — as little as 14 percent. Even 14 percent produces considerable intelligence, but if we can increase this even by a few percentage points, imagine the potential increase in our intelligence. This increase can be achieved slowly by pranic energy — the food for the marmas throughout the body.

The effect of this increase in intelligence is not simply to make the intellect sharper, but also to expand the boundaries of understanding beyond material existence. In other words, the mind becomes attuned to provide the foundation necessary for spiritual development. The system of energy channels we know as the chakras is opened. Using techniques for the conscious mind, the root chakra becomes unified with the crown chakra through the kundalini. Each chakra has its own distinct responsibilities and functions. These functions are compromised if the chakras are weakened by insecurity or fear.

Breathing Exercises
Strengthening the mind means strengthening the chakras, for mind and chakras depend on each other. To strengthen the chakras, we must utilize their connection with the marmas. The

technique to accomplish this is called *veerya mudra pranayama*. *Veerya* means internal power and has to do with the light inside the chakras and in the body. With it, the power of the conscious mind is expanded. The practice of veerya mudra pranayama is a most important practice because it increases everything in the body and mind — light, power, and spiritual emotions. The practice of veerya mudra pranayama completely opens up the divine and brings an experience of pure joy.

This particular pranayama is a unifying process and represents a complete understanding of the marma system in the body. When pranayama is done with this understanding, it benefits us physically, mentally, emotionally, psychologically, and spiritually. To prepare for these techniques, it is helpful to apply Marma Skincare cream to the face, if not the entire body.

PREPARATION: Choose a comfortable position on the floor, and sit either cross-legged or on the knees and calves, which allows for a straight spine. Apply Marma Skincare cream to the area between the eyebrows known as the third eye. Move from there around the eyebrows to the cheeks and nose, working down to the chin and neck and then around to the back of the neck.

Determine which nostril is open or closed by putting a finger on a nostril. If one nostril is closed, or only partially opened, this indicates that the hemisphere of the brain opposite to that nostril is not functioning optimally, and the electromagnetic current is not being efficiently produced by the body's generator, bringing fatigue. To open the nostril and increase the flow of air, take a deep breath, then breathe out alternately through each nostril. Repeat three times. By then, the nose should be opened.

While doing this breathing technique, your mind should be focused on the effects within your body. When performing this particular procedure to open the nostrils, the marmas are being stimulated. Visualize this process in your imagination, and be conscious of the marmas as they are being stimulated.

With your spine straight and erect, gently press the right side of the nose with the thumb of the right hand and close the *pingali*, or right nostril. Slowly inhale through the *ida*, or left nostril, until the lungs are full. This practice should be extremely slow and gentle. After inhaling, retain the air in the lungs. Then close the ida, or left nostril, with both the third and fourth fingers, and breathe out slowly and completely through the pingali, or right nostril. Breathe in through the *pingali*, hold, close the pingali and breathe out through the ida. Repeat this procedure for a total of twelve in-and-out breaths. The ida and pingali act as two walls to support the energy passage all the way through the spine.

While doing this pranayama technique, imagine the energy is going through the nostril into the hemisphere on the opposite side of the brain and up to the crown chakra. From there it descends to the kundalini at the base of the spine. As you hold the breath, have in your awareness that the energy is flowing through your body. As the breath goes out, follow its energy with your mind until the impurities are released from the body. Repeat this mental pattern as you take breath in through the opposite nostril. While inhaling each time, prana is waking up the eight marmas that are directly connected to the seven chakras. The purity of these marmas is very important for awakening the chakras.

As I have said, the human body can be divided into air, fire, and water. Now you can see that breathing, mantras, mudras, and other religious practices correlate with the air, or mental aspect. Meditation and using herbal formulas help to improve the aura, corresponding to the fire, or spiritual side. Taking the herbs and doing the exercises takes care of the water, or physical side. Basically, we are balancing the nervous system, the heart and cardiovascular system, and the endocrine system. These are all controlled by one thing — the marmas.

CHAPTER TWELVE

Rejuvenation with Marma Science

When I was a child, one of our most important prayers was for the divine light to shine on us, to wake up our light inside and make us brilliant for God. I remember that in our supplications we gave praise for the amazing God who had given us the same light as the light in plants and herbs. Years later, after I formulated Marma Skincare cream and used it with daily exercises, meditation, and prayer, I knew that there were natural ways to strengthen our abilities and our soul's connection to God's divine light.

Everywhere we look, into ancient or new concepts, many of the technologies are based on light. Certain combinations of plants can bring out the light from the different chakras, which are associated with different colors. This light can scintillate with life in our daily practices and transfuse us with joy in special marma treatments. This is internal beauty.

In olden times, a consultation would be done by a group of specialists at court - *vaidyas* (physicians), astrologers, and masters for spiritual guidance. Experts in this knowledge took care of the kings and queens in all facets of vitality. The one who became master of the marma could do all of this at once. Such masters were considered to be the most valuable in the kingdom, so much so that the royalty would give them half their land to retain their service. This is the same concept design of quality that I am introducing in my practice.

My programs — **Energy Reading with Harmonizing Herbal Program**, 7-session **Healing Program**, and **Rejuvenation Program** —are all vehicles for regaining health. Practices which can be done at home in order to balance physical cleansing (simple but effective exercise), mental cleansing and development (breathing), and spiritual development (meditation, mudras, mantras) were described in Chapters Ten and Eleven. When all the levels of a person are cleansed and integrated, homeostasis is achieved. When there is a natural balance, spirituality and beauty are in symmetry.

The **Harmonizing Herbal Program** is a 21-day set of herbal tea blends and herbal massage oils recommended for each person according to planetary influences from birth as well as in the present time. For the most rapid progress, this program can be done once a month if desired. A general guideline is to repeat the Herbal Program up to seven times to go through the seven layers of the body and the seven chakras.

An **Energy Reading** can be done as well, during which an accurate assessment of the person's energy field is done to determine where blockages are located and the consequent effects on the psychology and physiology.

How many times in a year would someone have an Energy Reading? Nature has seasonal changes four times a year. Planetary influences also change four times in a year. Dividing the twelve months by the four cycles is a good way to monitor progress. Every three months, reading the energy blockages along with the planetary positions affecting the marmas can map out the influences for the next four months. To keep up regularly, the beginning of each of the four seasons is a good time to check the marmas for blockages that may result, not only from planetary changes, but environmental and earth changes as well.

An herbal tune-up every three months determines where blockages are and adjusts for the different factors so that balance can be restored in our lives. One of the main benefits of the herbs is the absorption of the exact nutrients which are necessary for the individual. According to planetary influences, changes occur at the dietary level. This is why it is extremely important to keep up a routine.

Some people are born with acidity. Some people have certain problems during the month. Nutritional deficiencies are calculated and recommendations are made with consideration for the body's metabolism. In addition, there are financial influences in our lives that can be factored in. Astrology for couples can determine the synastry of people in relation to each other. The chemistry imbalance between people can be corrected with the herbs.

Preventing problems for the next three months can save much in time and trouble. I have seen the effects of natural disasters in people's energy fields, and I have felt them myself. Many of the difficulties that have happened to them disappear or become easier once they start the Herbal Program. Releasing the blockage every three months at the right time will help to prevent the aging process. Very often, people wear an expensive gemstone according to their astrology, only the gemstone alone is not enough. The blockages must also be released in a timely manner, otherwise it is like covering a cut or wound on the hand without putting any stitches in it. During an energy reading, the advice for wearing the right stones is also given, but as a part of the whole picture.

Each of the herbal blends is working on one of the seven different areas of the body, the marma. Usually, the customized herbs are adjusted according to the individual's blockages. Approximately ninety different herbs are blended in various combinations. The Harmonizing Herbal Program is taken for three weeks, which represent body, mind, and spirit. Because these unique blends work with the subtle energies, they have an incredible effect on every aspect of the twenty-one important marmas of the body.

As influences change every three months, each person will have a different experience depending on what time they were born. In this respect, an Energy Reading every three months will cover the accurate calculations and right recommendations for the present time. The tea blends are taken one tablespoon at a time in the morning and evening. In order to balance the energy externally, a different oil is applied each week. The oils are optional, but extremely effective in combination with the teas.

Please see figure 26 in the center of this book
[Energy of the Triangle]

All of these herbs are commonly available, but the important distinction is the preparation of the formulas and the concept of administering them with a deep understanding of energy blockages.

> R. P. of La Costa, California, noticed these results:
> The teas have an amazing effect on my sense of well-being. There was a visible difference because people were asking me, "What are you doing? You look so different." Someone close died . . . My whole system calmed and my emotions were calmed. After all that occurred, the teas really lifted my depression. My mind was so scattered and it really helped me focus on my life.

> J. K. of Sonoma, California, enjoys the herbs and oils:
> With the oils, I found myself feeling really sensual and really natural. I felt very much in my body. It had such a calming effect.

> T. C. of Alberta, Canada, said this about the Herbal Program:
> I've been experiencing joy. It's very subtle - but I'm very aware of it. It's not from any one experience, but more of an expression coming from within. Maybe my heart is opening up more. It's bringing up stuff that needs to be released, which temporarily interrupted my joy and bliss. But I understand that the old stuff is on its way out. I have a massage therapist who can tell a lot through his touch and he noticed definite improvement in my body.

> I really appreciate how subtle the Herbal Program is. I really like the way this works. I'm doing things that I've been wanting to do and now I have the courage to do them.

Despite individual and cultural differences, human bodies are basically the same. We can divide the human body into three characteristics, which correspond to body/mind/spirit. That is the basic triangle.

DIVIDING TRIANGLE INTO SEVEN

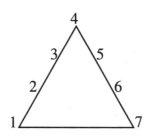

Starting from the left corner of the triangle, go up to the apex and down the other side. Divide the triangle into seven, with 4 at the top. Starting from the left, it goes 1, 2, 3, 4, indicating work on the first four chakras and first four layers of the body. A person needs very good emotional support during the four initial sessions in a rejuvenation program because this is when the negative side gets worked upon. Once the fourth session is over, levels 5, 6, and 7 are on the positive side and therefore much easier.

Anybody who has gone through the **Healing Program** has probably experienced an initial hesitation. Many people, when they first come to see me, put up resistance, even starting fights and competition. "I am not going to let you cure me!" This is especially true for those with more marma blockages. Then, after four sessions, they say, "Oh, I feel better in the stomach; I feel better in my mind." The first three sessions correspond to the lower chakras. The fourth session deals with the heart chakra, which is the pivotal point. The upper three chakras are much lighter.

We all have negative and positive sides. The positive side is very gentle and diplomatic; the negative side is always holding back. The positive side is polite; the negative side is resistant. Negative people always resist change in themselves and others. This conflict between positive and negative is within all of us. This is known as yin and yang, masculine and feminine, or *Purusha* and *Prakriti*.

Once when I was seeing clients in San Diego, I was looking

for a candidate for my very special longevity treatment. I wanted to show how rapidly someone can be rejuvenated to a prime condition. In order to best demonstrate my treatment, I needed a person with several complications. Out of more than one thousand people, there was one woman who was eminently qualified. Just before we were to begin treatment, she left and never came back. She just looked at me strangely and disappeared. If she had only completed the first program, she would have thought, "Okay, I want to do it!" The Rejuvenation is a very strenuous treatment; it is a strain on me and a strain on the person, but the results are a remarkable rejuvenation in a very short time. Her negative side would not allow her to do it. She lost the opportunity for a complete and very rare series of beauty treatments.

Although it came as a surprise to me in the beginning, I understand that there is a resistance to change in all of us. Inside, we know that a program is going to work, but still we try to get away from it. This resistance is built up in our body from the physical blockages incurred in childhood. Those blockages hold us back from moving into our positive nature. This same resistance can be seen between people, which is another form of blockage. The negative side has a strong influence in slowing our progress. Try to accept the positive side even though it might seem weaker, despite the fact that it contains more light. It is also good to work with the psychology of transformation as blockages are released. In the Healing Program, I sometimes request that the client get support from a competent psychologist.

Aging

Our chakras are the generators of all the energies stored and distributed in every part of the body. Each chakra has a different duty, different work to do. Our body also has seven different layers. Each of those layers is connected to the energy centers. For example, the energy connected to the artery helps the flow of new cells with the veins replacing the old cells. The nerves activate the process of arteries and veins, or heart. Our endocrine system, which is the spirit, takes care of the hormone supply, controlling the emotions, processing the right things for the physical and mental body and fulfilling our pleasures. As our brain absorbs the energy for our mind, the stomach absorbs the physical energy for the physical body. They are all connected to each other. Any disruption in any system will affect the process of replacement of cells. When the old cells accumulate in different parts of the body, that part will become weaker.

When we have problems with life in general, our mind also carries toxins. When the wrong spiritual practice is followed, it is like eating unwanted food for the soul. That will bring us into negative and fanatic thinking, which pollutes the soul. Excessive stress or mentally disturbing images like violent movies pollute our mind and the mind becomes toxic. This will cause aging of the body, mind, and soul. By taking care of this triad, which is the marmas, we can maintain this triangle properly. We can age in a healthy way and leave this physical body to choose a tender, vital body in a very short time, usually forty-one days after death. One who has done the right things in this life and lived a positive life will get a new body soon after the forty-one days. Others may extend for more time and have to take what is available. Doing positive things reserves the right place for our spirit to choose the next life.

Energy Work

No matter how a human body has been shaped by heredity and environment, my programs can produce beneficial changes. The results are amazing to see. Treatment is often divided into seven sessions, working on one layer of the body during each session. A client's appearance and demeanor are very different after each of the sessions. As the successive layers are cleared, 99 percent of the people tell of their experience with emotional changes.

Marmas are divided into seven different marma layers, each of which is worked on during successive sessions:

Arterial marma activates the construction of new cells.
Venous marma activates the cleansing of old cells and toxins.
Nerve tissue marma activates the flow of electromagnetic current.
Lymph and plasma marma activates the nourishing fluids.
Flesh marma activates the muscle fiber, ligaments, tendons, and fat.
Joint marma activates the areas of contact between bones.
Bone marma activates the bone and soft tissue within bone structures.

When energy blockages are being released, each level of the marmas is stimulated.

The seventh session involves the *Shukra marma*. We are now working on the whole marma system. Here we see the negative and positive sides, as well as the triple aspects of the human body:

Endocrine	Spirit	Air	Vata
Nervous	Mind	Fire	Pitta
Vascular	Body	Water	Kapha

The doshas balance the five elements. The five elements function by the stimulation of the seven chakras, which regulate the flow of energy through the 107 marmas.

I have created a 3-month series of programs which work on the three systems of the body. There is also a 7-month series of programs for deeper work on the seven layers. The self-care and treatment programs both work on the marmas and give beneficial effects because they are reaching the subtle energy level of the body.

> This story is from T. S. of Cypress, California, who was inspired to write:
> When I first came to Joseph, I was suffering with sciatica in my lower back which I could feel in both of my legs. My disks were in bad shape and every step was painful. I had a myriad of other problems that seemed to get worse as I became older.
>
> I will never forget our first meeting. I was greeted by a quiet man whose eyes glowed with wisdom and love as I had never seen. In spite of Joseph's soft-spoken demeanor, I could feel I had been guided to a very powerful healer. Without words from me describing my problems, Joseph knew where I had been suffering in my body.

Not only did Joseph's herbs and oils take away the physical pain, but it purged out mental toxins and suffering I had held deep within me for many years. The trouble of pinched nerves dissipated and my back became flexible, supple and free of the pain. I became physically more active and a lot happier. I felt Joseph had taken away much of my misery.

I enrolled in Joseph's summer Healing Program in Newport Beach. The treatments he gave me were incredible. I do not exaggerate when I say that I could feel bursts of energy from his hand as he worked. Hours after his treatments, I could feel sensations of energy drumming like great waves through my head and body.

Joseph's treatments opened the energy pathways (marmas) so that my body could begin healing. After the treatment cycle, my body began to change by leaps and bounds. It helped my organs to function normally and my mind to be free of suffering. I noticed my ability to absorb food improved so much that I was able to cut back on the supplements. I also began to intuitively eat differently, keeping my diet balanced. In addition, I look younger, feel younger and have an inner beauty that is evolving out of me. The deep lines on my forehead have nearly disappeared and my body lost all the extra pounds it could never lose.

I can honestly say that Joseph's healing treatments, herbs and oils not only saved my life, but gave me a quality of life I had not ever had before. I continue to improve in health and I know I will continue to do so because of Joseph's treatments that are not oriented towards short-term treating, but long-term healing of body, mind and soul.

By looking at a person's aura, we can see which part of the body has blockages. The blocked energy also shows on the face since the face is connected to all the organs of the body. One can feel this energy — where it is flowing freely and where it is blocked.

When I work on a client, there are different, dynamic effects in each of the chakras. According to the blockages, the energetic changes show in the aura. When I work on people, the colors correspond to the ongoing transformation.

Other than herbal synergistics, touch is the secret for freeing the life force. Of course, this ability has to be given as a gift from a previous master and then passed along in succession to another. There is an energy transfer when one specifically touches another and releases the blockages. The special vital areas on the body are kept very secret because in martial arts they are also used in self-defense.

When an injury occurs directly on certain marmas, illness can result. By finding where the injured marma is located, the nature of the trauma and even the exact time of the occurrence can be ascertained. Accordingly, a master can take care of the problem. For example, a person can be twenty-five or thirty years old and have the skin of a sixty year-old as a result of physiologic imbalances and blockages in the body. When the blockages are accurately released, the person can attain balance and once again look his or her proper age. When all the systems are practiced, a person can achieve enlivened energy and greater abilities.

In India, tradition holds that nothing is put on one's skin unless it has been prepared by a master. That is the distinct specialty of marma beauty care; it is the same as it was in the ancient times of kings and queens, who closely protected the masters of Marma Science as the providers of quintessential health and beauty treatments.

We derive such wonderful benefits when the light energy, the electromagnetic current, is flowing through our marma system. Our lives blossom in all areas and we can reach our true potential.

> G. D. of San Diego, California, said this after the Healing Program:
> I have a renewed sense of vigor and vitality that I have not experienced since childhood. I am losing weight without even trying, and naturally eating foods that are good. My thinking used to be fuzzy, but now it is much clearer. My legs were swollen with edema, but

now they look normal. I released so many emotional things that held me back all my life. Everything is balancing out; the clock is turning back and my body is rebuilding. My body, mind, and spirit are eternally grateful from the top of my head to the tips of my toes. I feel great and look wonderful. I am thankful and bless Joseph.

S. C. of San Francisco, California, was pleasantly surprised:
After the program, I went to New York on business. Home Shopping Network carries one of our products. Usually, when I have to speak in front of people, I get very nervous. I guess it's fear of judgment and a common human reaction. But this time was different. I was completely relaxed and natural about being in front of TV cameras. Afterward, people came up and complimented me and asked if I would do voice-overs. I know this is a result of working with Joseph and I'm both surprised and very pleased to be free of that fear.

R. E. of Berkeley, California, made these observations:
This is a very powerful program. It goes very deep. My soul really likes this stuff! It may not always be comfortable, but that's a part of waking up.

The energy and clearing is on a very deep level and I'm very appreciative of it. It feeds me in a very big way. The system is awesome and very, very clean. There are other powerful systems, but they are not always clean in terms of an energetic point of view. You can't take someone somewhere that you've never been before. He's obviously done his work to be able to this for other people. There are very few masters on earth. My hat's off to him.

J. V. of San Carlos, California, wrote these words:
I became acquainted with Joseph Kurian a little over six months ago. I volunteered to test his skin care line for one month and be videotaped before and after using the products. I wasn't having any particular health problems

at the time, but I was experiencing a number of blocks in my personal and professional life and felt in need of spiritual healing.

During the time I was testing Joseph's skin care system, I met with him several times. I noticed early on that, after spending a few minutes in his presence, I began to feel calm, free, and spontaneous. Increasingly, I felt youthful and joyful whenever we talked and laughed together. Joseph has an energetic gift which I have seen in few people: when I was with him, I always felt better about myself and more confident that everything would work out for me. I wish to stress that this increasing sense of confidence and comfort was not so much because of anything in particular that Joseph said or did as it was the sense of godliness, joy, and love which I felt in his energy field. This positive energy was so powerful in its calm radiance that I found my own energy effortlessly rising, lightening and filling with love.

Joseph told me that I had blockages in my third and fourth chakras, and that he believed a weekend healing program would benefit me. I took the marma rejuvenation weekend this past September.

This weekend was unlike anything else I have ever experienced. I saw Joseph once the first day and twice a day for three days for marma treatments. My treatment sessions with Joseph were joyful for me. I felt a deep level of trust building with every treatment, and he was invariably sensitive, respectful and loving towards me. In between treatments, my emotions did some pretty wild rollercoastering. It wasn't at all unusual for me to be ecstatic in the morning and paranoid in the evening! I even had an experience which closely resembled a panic attack on Monday morning, prior to my final treatments. Joseph said that this represented a cleansing of old feelings and memories, and was a very positive sign. I left at the end of the weekend knowing that I had experienced something unforgettable.

It has now been close to four months since my marma treatment weekend. I noticed that for the first four weeks or so following the weekend, I was in a very joyful and serene frame of mind. This was followed by about four weeks characterized by a lot of anger and agitation. I seemed particularly sensitive to my environment and easily irritated. Since this period passed, I have become calmer and seem to be on a steady emotional keel.

I've also been experiencing guidance at a subtle level about things I can do for myself to further my own healing and growth. I've been led to certain books and exercise programs. Recently, I received the message that I needed to see one of my sisters and make amends for something which occurred in our childhood. Would I have gotten these messages if I hadn't taken the marma weekend? I can't be certain, but I do feel that my body has been cleansed of some very draining and negative emotions which impeded my spiritual progress, diverted badly needed energy, and prevented me from living in the present.

I am very grateful that I met and worked with Joseph. I use his skin care system exclusively and would unhesitatingly recommend him and his work to anyone who is in need of physical or spiritual healing. To my mind, he is an outstanding example of a human being who is living his highest purpose. I have found in my life that there are certain teachers with whom I can change just by being in their presence or reading their words. Joseph Kurian is definitely one of these people in my life. My spirit takes steps forward just from spending time with him. I would encourage anyone who is struggling with any type of healing issue to consult Joseph. He embodies a beautiful description by Iyanla Vanzant of the compassionate person: "When you are a powerful master of yourself, you know that what you give is of the universal divine energy flowing through you. It is not yours. It belongs to life. When a powerful person gives life, s/he knows they cannot be depleted. Instead, they know they are being strengthened. You must be strong in order to be compassionate."

Clearing the Information Channels

As profound as the changes can be during a **Rejuvenation Program**, there is a simple analogy that explains the process of clearing and restoring the marma circuitry. Our psychophysiology is very much like a biocomputer. We make logical and creative decisions constantly, based on simple yes or no choices, like the binary system of a computer. We also access information that we have stored from previous experiences.

The computer has chips and circuitry that save and relay data. Occasionally, we delete some files. In our human body, chakras can be considered our computer chips, storing our past memories, both good and bad. When we experience frustration or store misguided information inside the system, it hurts and takes up too much space. The old memories need to be deleted from our bodies just as we clean out old data from the computer. Anyone who has worked with computers has most likely had nonsense hieroglyphics show up on the screen as a result of corrupt or fragmented files. Sometimes, it even becomes necessary to clean out the hard drive and reformat. When the correct files are restored, information flows logically and intelligently. Common sense and creativity are natural choices.

Each of our chakras has certain fixed information, plus any new memories we add. Some are really a waste of space and time. Each of the different chakras holds different memories, and each of the layers of the body carries or utilizes information which is sent from the chakras. For example, each of the layers can carry toxins. Then the information coming from the chakras cannot go into or through the congested marma layers. Confusion results, as nourishment is not delivered and different areas of the body/mind start to malfunction. We start to lose our natural abilities and energy, our senses become dulled, and there is no joy.

In the Rejuvenation Program, the blockages, which are really unnecessary and inaccurate information, are cleared so the current can once again flow through. False beliefs and accumulated traumas are deleted. People are frequently surprised to find that they no longer react to negative trigger situations. Instead, they enjoy a new-found freedom and proceed to establish a new set of goals.

Working with thousands of clients over the years, I have observed how ancient marma knowledge clears our biocomputers. Taking time and making the effort to do the Rejuvenation Program allows us to achieve a new, clarified mind — like the newest computer chip — more available memory that can recall unlimited, joyous potential.

Kaya Kalpa

Kaya Kalpa is the most effective applied science of rejuvenation practiced on earth. It is the culmination of the marma system, Dhanur Veda and Ayur Veda, the knowledge of gemstones, astrology, mantric power, and the power of breath. Kaya Kalpa has been practiced in India since ancient times. Years of my research and personal practice with clients have helped me rediscover this powerful, transformational rejuvenation.

A practitioner of Kaya Kalpa needs to reach the ultimate level in all these combined sciences, developed through discipline in body and mind, in order for the effects of Kaya Kalpa to be fully realized. For example, repeating mantras ten times a day can provide some stimulation of the energy in the body, but when the mantra is repeated one hundred and one times a day, an incredible vibrational energy is created which connects with the whole universe. By utilizing this universal power supply, the energy system deep in the core of a human body can be awakened. So, even in the marma system, one still has to do practices. But in Kaya Kalpa, those who receive the treatments have nothing to do other than to accept the benefits. The easiest, most comfortable rejuvenation technique that exists in the world can simply be experienced.

> K. G. of Piedmont, California, is now free of a list of limitations:
> You know, as I was thinking about how different my life is from before I met Joseph, I started to cry. Not sadness, but tears of joy, relief, gratitude. Let me fill you

in on my amazing progress! Beginning with my head, I have more hair. It was receding around my face kind of like a man's. It was thinner as well. Now it is fuller and healthier. Also, I had really bad headaches. Sometimes I would have the same headache for days, and around the time of my period I would get horrible migraines. Now I can't remember when I had my last headache. Isn't that wonderful? My neck had been bothering me off and on for probably about 20 years. I was in several car accidents where I got whiplash and I was waking up three and four times a night in pain and taking muscle relaxers and sleep aids. Now I don't even need medication and I sleep through the night.

As far as my back, for the last 4 years, it had been going out for weeks at a time. When it was out, I couldn't drive, sit, or stand for very long or really enjoy much of anything. The pain was so unmanageable, I would get depressed. Since my first program with Joseph, my back has not gone out. That is a miracle. No one who knows me can believe I am the same person.

My healing for my back is wonderful, but there is something for which I am even more grateful. From the time I was thirteen, I had painful, long periods with a very irregular cycle. As I got older, my symptoms increased. I tried all kinds of herbs, acupuncture, muscle relaxers, vitamins, as well as every type of pain medication. Nothing helped and my periods were getting worse all the time. There is no way to put into words how this healing has changed my life.

Writing all this out in black and white is unbelievable. I can't believe what I lived through and I can't believe the healing I have received. I can't wait to do more work with Joseph! Each time things are better. I guess it is obvious just from seeing the physical aspects of my healing that there would be corresponding emotional/mental and spiritual benefits. Thank God, I can wake up hopeful now, looking forward to my days and my life. I am doing things

I have not done in years. I used to not be able to take walks because my Achilles tendon was so sore. Now I can walk every day if I want to. I love to walk outdoors — that was something I had really missed. I was basically cooped up physically, and emotionally, and now I am getting out and enjoying life.

J. L. of San Francisco, California, gained this perspective: One of the most amazing things that Joseph told me was that my energy was very scattered. That was so accurate. After he worked on me, I was much more able to focus and I felt as though I was controlling and directing my energy instead of my energy controlling and directing me. Another major aspect was the personal issue that had to do with feeling insecure. A lot of my inner insecurity was the result of stored memories and mental and emotional blockages. Once they were cleared, my sense of insecurity was greatly lessened and I now approach life with a whole new level of confidence.

While this doesn't happen overnight, when I look back on the time just prior to working with Joseph, I am amazed by the difference. I also feel as though I am able to access my potential and realize it. I was one of the classic cases where people would often say "You have so much potential," which when you look at it is just another way to say "underachiever." Now I do not feel like my abilities are locked up inside of me and I am far more free and able to express and demonstrate them.

I believe that this work was a major, major breakthrough that allowed for all of this to happen. The shift in the subtle body takes a while to reverberate and likewise shift you on all the other levels. But that is the only way to go deep enough to make that deep and definitive shift.

This Vedic medicine of India goes beyond religion. It is a science, an ancient alchemy. The masters have methods of developing the body energetically so that the personality shines through with a powerful charisma. **The basis of this transformation is rare herbal formulas which are prepared with the powders of precious gemstones according to precise, time-tested traditions.** There is a potent form of electrical energy contained in the herbal preparations that harmonizes with the energy centers of the body to waken the chakras and activate the brain. This is the energy of the triangle that strengthens the body, relaxes the mind, and frees the spirit. The formulas are used in conjunction with a very sophisticated stimulation of the marma centers of the body.

Herbs

The herbs which are prepared for Kaya Kalpa are authentic and carefully cultivated in absolutely organic conditions. Some of them are picked precisely at certain times of the year, during the full moon, in the middle of the night, by people who are totally naked. The harvesters are not even supposed to wear shoes so that the energy connects with that of Earth.

Even the shape of the earth in that area has to be specially prepared in terms of its vata, pitta, and kapha — air, fire, and water. Hills, flat surfaces, and water have to be joined together in a place that is an energy center of the earth. In that specific area, the herbs are grown and picked. Exact timing governs their planting, growth, and harvesting. Three to four years of drying in the sun and months of curing in caves beneath the ground serve to harness the energies of heaven and earth. Thousands of plants produce only a small amount of extract.

The herbs have to be kept in the sunlight for a minimum of forty-one days or a maximum of four and one-half years. The herbs continue to absorb more energy for as long as they are cured. There are certain processes used to absorb the energy from the planets and sun, and other practices used to throw off bad energy and retain good energy.

Please see figure 27 in the center of this book
[Astrobotanicals]

Astrological calculations are used to determine which planets are blocking the person undergoing treatment; then herbs are mixed to counteract the planetary effects. The precious formulas

— prepared correctly and applied to the body in certain areas of the marmas — can entirely rebuild a human body.

Astrology is again consulted to determine the most beneficial times for the purification of the herbs. While performing the rituals for these rarefied herbal/gemstone formulas, there should be special circumstances regarding the atmosphere in the area. Even the air itself must be cleansed since it contains positive and negative elements. Creating an area in which to prepare the herbs is like creating a very special world. The circumference around the area is extremely sensitive to any negative or positive vibration. Any person or animal entering this area has to have a proper, purified body. We do not make these herbal preparations in front of anyone because even spoken words can affect the herbs.

Puja means purifying the atmosphere where the formulas are prepared. When the herbs are drying, absorbing the energy of the sun, that area has to be totally purified, which is done by burning certain herbs. Placing plants and trees in the right proportions can attract a universal energy into that specific part of the earth. These measures can prevent any kind of unnatural, negative influence from anywhere in the universe. A ritual of herbal purification is repeated until the treatment herbs contain a very refined energy. It takes time for the good energy from the planets to be absorbed; that energy will be amplified in the person who is undergoing the treatment.

Indian Ritual

Wealth can be measured in money or more precious commodities like health and wisdom. Some of the so-called "third world" countries have healthy lifestyles and very wise people. Masters of the ancient traditions are some of these people. Spirit exists in great beings who have this traditional knowledge. Spirit will remain where there is more spirituality.

Why do so many spiritual people come from India? Indian cities are heavily congested. Even with the congestion, heat, traffic, and all the difficulties, once you land in India, you may be surprised and amazed at what you find. The Spirit itself changes inside you because there is a network of spiritual sustenance in the air. Everywhere, every aspect of India has Spirit. You can smell it. You can feel it.

In every corner of India, even though people are very busy, they stop to show their respect to the deities. They have incense or herbs burning in front of the deities. That way Spirit can have its food, which is incense that is prepared from ancient recipes of purifying herbal smoke. The respect people give to Spirit comes from inside themselves and brings out their own spirit. The herbal smoke goes to the brain so the spirit is stimulated and the electromagnetic current in the brain is activated.

Twelve thousand year-old ancient traditions are well-designed and well-preserved in every aspect of Indian life. When we look with a positive attitude, we learn universal values. The concept of spirituality at the heart of the participation. For example, when we go into old churches where frankincense is burning, our nervous systems are cooled down. In a similar fashion, during some of the pujas for morning worship on every street corner of India, the combination of herbs that are burned are perfectly balanced to feed the Spirit of the universe, which is the electromagnetic system, and purify it.

Anyone who has this treatment will experience remarkable changes in their body. In forty-one days their eyes, teeth and color of the nose all improve; blue veins on the legs fade away; bone density increases substantially; hair, tissues, and muscles become healthy and vibrant; all the organs are revitalized resulting in balanced functioning of the digestive tract so that one should be able to eat any kind of food; the intestine and colon, liver, spleen, pancreas, thyroid, gall bladder, and adrenals are restored to good condition.

The mental effects of years of trauma that one has gone through dissipate. Different patterns that may have persisted for a long time can be released, from child abuse, sexual abuse, or any kind of addiction such as drugs, heroin, alcohol, and wrong foods. Absolute mental clarity opens the awareness and sharpens the focus.

Blockages occurring from the time of birth are cleared out. Many miraculous benefits manifest as latent abilities come out and people fulfill their potential destiny. People who are shy discover social satisfaction. There is a core of courage in everyone that is awakened and motivates the expression of unique talents.

GEMSTONES

Kaya Kalpa is one of the most powerful treatment systems based on gemstone frequencies. It is far more profound than crystals used by people in the West for their drinking water or decorative display. Kaya Kalpa is the ultimate transformation. We can even change our destiny when we go through the system of Kaya Kalpa.

An individual's physiology and astrology are carefully examined in order to choose specific gemstones, such as diamonds, rubies, and sapphires, which are then prepared with a customized process, designed especially for that person. It is similar to the way that every faceted diamond is unique. For each of the planets, there is a corresponding gemstone. A person's astrological signs and positions are calculated in conjunction with planetary positions. The herbs and gems are then prepared according to these calculations.

Pictures of the Indian Maharajas and Maharanis show them wearing many jewels, but these were not for adornment. Different gemstones were worn on different parts of their bodies to reinforce body, mind, and spirit. The jewels were worn very consciously to activate and conduct the life force on the subtle energy level. The king or queen had to wear ornaments based on their planetary connections — exactly the same jewels which were divided into molecules for their Kaya Kalpa. Each specific stone was placed in a specific place according to the energy coming from the corresponding planet which would directly affect that area. Some energies can be released through the wearing of special gemstones on the body.

Sometimes removing a gemstone has beneficial effects. One day I had a consultation with a woman who was perfectly healthy, except for a problem related to her urinary tract. She had tried everything to find a remedy before she finally came to me. During the visit, I told her that the ring she was wearing was causing her problem. When I told her to remove the ring, which her grandmother had given to her, she was not happy about it. She did not have a clue about astrology at the time I met her. Once she removed the ring, her problem was gone. She could have bought several fine rings for all the tests she had been through.

For royalty, some stones were worn on hats because those areas were connected with marmas in the head, improving that person's consciousness so he or she could be the most intelligent leader. You can see the effects in the photos of Maharajas and Maharanis, in how beautiful their eyes are and how powerful they appear.

Please see figures 28-30 in the center of this book
[Majarajas wearing gemstones]

Nine gemstones and an equal amount of gold, mixed with herbs and burned into ash forms a very special combination. The stones selected could be diamonds, rubies, or whatever gemstones are indicated according to the astrological effects on the individual. After that, a process of distillation captures the vibrational frequencies at a molecular level, so the gold and gemstones become a molecular infusion.

A process with gold fortifies the potency of the stones and involves accurate timing for the induction of positive planetary energies into the particles. These particles are divided on a molecular level until the atomic structure is compatible with that of the chakras. In this way, universal energies can be distributed throughout the physical body. All the formulas, knowledge, and processes are involved in creating customized blends for clients.

Gemstones become jewels of energy after they are burned at high temperatures. Ultimately, they reach an ash form wherein they are as potent as medicine. When gemstones are prepared along with herbs, and burned to a certain degree, the combination produces a tremendous energy. The preparation has to be kept for several months or longer.

Please see figures 31 and 32 in the center of this book
[Capturing energy of gemstones]

The gemstone powders and herbal extracts are fortified with chanting and mantras. These blessings translate to actual physical results through the repetition of vocal sound. Months of chanting create a configuration of energy in the air that surrounds and covers the energetic substance. This energy matrix has the qualities of the triangle and mingles with the energy fields of those who do the mantric practice. All this energy mixed together imbues the herbal preparations with highly concentrated subtle frequencies. The long, involved preparation of alchemical ingredients is the reason Kaya Kalpa has been very, very rare. This is perhaps the most expensive treatment in the world, and the most exquisite. With Kaya Kalpa, at the time of death, a person has the right to choose who he or she will be in the next life. This is immortality.

A Gemstone Ritual

Once, while I was preparing the Kaya Kalpa formulas, something miraculous happened — the most magnificent thing I have ever seen on earth. I had taken forty-one days to prepare a particular herbal combination, and it turned out to be perfect. Preparations for this special herbal medicine were undertaken in a purified place. During that time, the whole area became suffused with golden light. The light grew until the whole surrounding area, including myself, was covered with this golden light, the color of the aura that is inside all of us. That same golden aura mingled with that of the planets, the sun, and the earth.

All five elements contributed to this aura and created a very pure atmosphere while I was doing the puja and the *homas*, burning certain herbs to purify the entire surface of the area involved. Depending on how large the homa, that much of the earth is purified at one time. The purification can cover an area as small as one hundred square feet or as large as one million square feet. In this instance, an area of approximately ten square feet was involved and, within that area, one square foot became totally golden light.

The energy continued to change with the image of the various gems reflected in the light. This indicated that the herbs had reached maximum absorption and had mingled with the universal energy completely. The energy was actually contained in a very safe material by a special process. After that, the essence which was to be applied to the human body was kept in an airtight container. All in all, the experience of the concentrated golden glow during this particular preparation for Kaya Kalpa was a magnificent experience.

J. K. of Sonoma, California, felt an energetic shift:
I found that the Rejuvenation Program made my body sink
into a really deep relaxation, and gave me a sense of myself as I really am, without a lot of the noise that had been
there before due to the tension. It was really pretty amazing to watch my body change so quickly and dramatically.
The most amazing thing about the Rejuvenation Program
for me was how, for the first time, I really felt comfortable
in my own skin. I settled down into my own body to the
point where I just felt happy and contented.

I'm a singer and my voice was much more grounded and
my breathing was stronger. After my Rejuvenation Program, I went back into my singing and back to my friends
and my life, and everything had been elevated to another
level because I had sunk more deeply into my true self,
into my body.

C. A. of San Francisco, California has a new-found respect
for the rejuvenation work:
I was a little skeptical at first because I had been to different doctors on different problems, but I opened myself up
because, first of all the skincare line had made such a difference in my complexion and how I felt about my skin
that I just thought I would give it a try. I can't, I don't want
to say "miracle" because that sounds too cliche-ish, but I
still have all the responsibilities. I still do everything I did
before, but I do it with a little more renewed vigor.

I feel better about myself. I feel like everything has shifted
and fallen into line. I don't know if that makes any sense,
but things feel better internally and I'm able to do more.
I'm just able to do more without the stress I was feeling
before. I was having backaches. I was having stomach problems. I still have a twinge of backache if I overdo or lift
something I shouldn't, which I fully understand. But so
much of the discomfort that I felt is gone, and I can't focus
in on anything except the Rejuvenation Program that I went
through with Joseph Kurian.

J. M. of Huntington Beach, California, wrote:
Five years ago when I met Joseph my life as a psychologist was going well, BUT, I had several problems that were causing me difficulty and interfering with my general well being and personal development. At age 59 I had had an acid stomach for about 5 years which with a number of alternative treatments had not healed, along with a life long tendency toward constipation, and I was having rather severe hot flashes. In addition, for several years I had been experiencing a circulation difficulty, as well as a depletion of energy, having frequent adrenal shots, and requiring rest and recuperation on the weekends. My face was showing signs of aging, with large clogged pores, bags under the eyes and rather pronounced crow's feet. Two - three years prior to meeting Joseph, I'd ignored a stiff neck, until one day it locked down giving me immense pain and difficulty in the bones, muscles and nerves. By the time I met Joseph, I was about 75-80% better, but still required monthly chiropractic adjustments. As a result of the neck injury, I'd stopped doing my yoga.

Joseph told me that my stomach was a factory and until it was working correctly, nothing else would. He also said a primary cause of my problems was in the gall bladder. I received immediate relief from the acid stomach and hot flashes, with an ongoing healing process deepening over several months. My face began to clear up, the skin was clear with normal pores, and glowed with a radiant light. Over several months, the wrinkles and bags under my eyes cleared, as my stomach and other organs were healing, level by level. My digestion and elimination have greatly improved, resulting in a reversal of the life long constipation. I have no menopausal symptoms, even though I've had no hormones and I look 10-15 years longer than I am. Within a short period of time, I no longer needed chiropractic adjustments.

A marvelous side effect was that my eyelashes grew! One day I'd laughingly told Joseph that I'd always wanted long black eyelashes and that if he'd handle the long, I'd handle the black! Imagine my surprise at 61 to suddenly have longer eyelashes than ever in my life. Another amazing change was that the skin on my nose totally has changed. Instead of large pores and blackheads, the skin has changed so that there is no longer anywhere for the blackheads to be.

A few days after my treatments with Joseph began, I told him that as a child I had stuttered. I had not experienced a dysfluency around Joseph, so you can imagine my surprise, where he merely replied, 'Yes, I know.' He said that I'd experienced a birth injury — I'd been a forceps baby and my aunt has told me that when my grandmother saw me she almost cried because my head was so banged up! So it all started there.

Over the past years, I've experienced emotional and spiritual changes that I didn't know to expect. My intuition and ability to see deep patterns of thinking and of behavior within my client's lives has greatly deepened. I merely ask within and receive information that is extremely helpful. Over the 5 years period I have become much more confident and clear in my thinking, and during the accelerated rejuvenation program, I touched very, very deep layers of fear and inadequacy and cried and cried for a couple of days. Then it was just gone. And it hasn't resurfaced. Since the rejuvenation program, something shifted within me and I have a new level of inner confidence and personal worth that replaces these negative belief systems- and it is very deep. I notice how this change affects almost every level of my life in very profound ways.

Most recently, about 5 months ago, I decided to start taking yoga classes again, having done only a minimal amount of stretching asanas since my injury of 7-8 years ago. My body loved the yoga and I noticed my body responding to the work in a way that it had not responded in my earlier practice. My bones and muscles seemed stronger! Strength and endurance were developing easily. I felt my body/mind somehow remembered the asanas, and the work with

Joseph had enabled my body to gain strength and stamina much more quickly than I had anticipated. I would have never thought I could reenter my yoga practice. Not bad for a 63 year old!

I feel as young and vital as I have ever felt. My life is very busy and full. I feel as though I have just begun to live and that I finally have something of value to contribute to Life. I have no plans to retire and I am excited about my next steps. I know my life has been enhanced because of my work with Joseph. I am forever grateful.

The Perfect Place

In order to utilize the precise molecular energy, the prepared essences have to be opened under supervised circumstances. While applying the substance to a recipient of Kaya Kalpa, additional energies from the sun or planets are not desirable. All that energy has already been infused in the herbs and now the formula should not be mixed with anything else or the effects will be changed.

In ancient times, Kaya Kalpa was only done under the earth in a very safe cave. The cave has to be located six feet down. The preparation of the cave is very involved. The earth must be made of pure clay, some of which is mixed with eighty-four different herbs in such a way as to create the consistency of mixing cement with water. The clay is mixed with the herbal extracts and the whole cave is plastered with this special clay. The cave becomes a totally safe place. Nothing can have an effect on it.

That exclusivity is intrinsic to Kaya Kalpa. In reality, a treatment must be done very securely, so as not to have any kind of influence other than the universal energy contained in the formula and the transference from the touch of the practitioner. My fourteen years of practice were primarily for the preparation of this mantric power, which is created inside the body and can be transferred through the hand to the other person. During actual treatment, this power comes through with a much higher intensity. Once the treatment is finished, the person undergoing treatment has to stay inside the cave, which is very comfortably made and has a regulated temperature. All the circumstances are balanced. Inside and out, very special herbs are burned to ensure that everything is purified properly.

The plants which are grown outside the cave have to be in a particular pattern, according to the ancient scriptures. These are very famous shapes that can be recognized in temples, and are imitated to determine where the plants are positioned. This formation has an additional energetic influence. All those rules are necessary to do the proper, original Kaya Kalpa treatment. These days it is not so easy to accomplish, but it is still possible.

I have done some Kaya Kalpa where, after the treatments, seventy-year-old people looked like they were fifty-five years old. The entire body had been replaced, and after seven to twenty-one days of treatment, the person's skin had changed and the bones were replaced. After three months, the entire set of nails was replaced with beautiful, strong nails. In some cases, gray hair changed back to its natural color. The heart was functioning very well and any kind of disease was eliminated. Even the entire bone marrow was replaced. Inside the marrow, as I have said, is where the electromagnetic current is stored. When the marrow is replaced, pure energy is centered there.

The recipients of Kaya Kalpa are taught spiritual practices, such as mantra and pranayama, and all these practices have to be followed. The fortunate recipients are not bored while doing this treatment – they feel absolute consciousness and bliss. They feel incredible joy, total health and well-being, and complete fulfillment. Every fiber of their body has its desires fulfilled right there, so they do not have any material desires. They are not unduly ambitious. They can enjoy their life, but are not anxious. On this earth, they are seeing heaven. That is how we can best describe the experience. After finishing the treatment, a person will be incredibly vibrant. His or her aura starts to glow.

Some of the Kaya Kalpa herbs have been adapted into my creams. My clients usually comment that their friends tell them they are glowing. The herbs are prepared in a traditional, systematic way, and only a relatively small amount creates an incredible effect. Imagine what the full Kaya Kalpa treatment can be – how powerful and how miraculous – the most precious wisdom preserved on earth.

I would like to create a place where this treatment can be available. People could share it with each other and learn how to create a beautiful, wonderful atmosphere. It gives me such pleasure to share this beautiful heaven that can be built on earth, to share this knowledge with others, even though it has been kept secret for so long. I really do fell that people deserve to have this information. I am fortunate to have been allowed access to his knowledge, and I know it is worthwhile to bring this magic wisdom into our lives on earth.

Please see figure A in the center of this book
[Center for Health and Evolution]

Part Four

The Cuisine of India

PART FOUR

The Cuisine of India

The people of South India have a fluid life style, following the rhythm of the four seasons. Without being overly strict about specific diets, they change their food intake according to the cycles of Nature. Just as you would not wear a winter coat in the summer, you would not eat the heavier foods of winter in the warm seasons. In this manner, the body becomes light and energetic so you can enjoy a greater variety of everything.

In my general contact with Westerners, I find that most are not very aware of India. Of course, people who do know about India realize that India has some of the world's most incredible cuisine. Many Western people misunderstand Indian food, thinking that Indian food is based on curry. Recently, I invited someone to my home and my guest asked if I put curry in the dinner. When we talk about Indian cuisine, a "curry" can refer to many different dishes.

Curry is a blend of many different spices, especially turmeric or saffron. Each of the curry contains at least ten different other spices as well, but turmeric is the main ingredient. Turmeric has wonderful effects: cleansing, purifying, protecting, and stimulating the skin. It even has the power to remove dead cells. When Indian children sustain bad injuries, their grandparents suggest drinking egg mixed with turmeric because it helps to rebuild tissues and cells. It also helps to build healthy cells externally.

Food

In Nature, God has made everything for us to enjoy. Personally, I have no special diet. One day I asked my master, "What foods should we not eat?" He told me, "Whatever will not eat your mouth while you are eating it." I believe, as did my ancestors, that everything on earth belongs to humans. God has given us all this marvelous bounty to enjoy and "re-create." Therefore, anything we put into our stomach develops into new cells. The body has the ability to analyze what is necessary and what is unnecessary for the body at the time. When our marmas function properly, our digestive organs decide what we need or do not need.

One day, I had a client call me and by the sound of her voice I could tell she was very guilty about something. When I asked her what happened, she said, "Joseph, I had a hamburger this morning." I asked her what was wrong with that. She said, "I thought it was junk food." I had only one thing to say to her, "There is no such thing as junk food. It depends on the condition of your digestion that morning." She said her digestion was fine and she felt good. I told her, "Then the food is not going to be junk in your stomach. Your stomach will digest it and the intestine will absorb what is necessary. The rest will be rejected naturally."

When you look at a hamburger, what is in it? Bread, meat, vegetable, cream, sour taste, onion (excellent for strength and vitality), and cheese. Add potato and this covers everything you need for your body to have a perfectly well-balanced diet. If you dine at the most well-arranged dinner table, you will not be eating more than this. The difference is that they eat ten times more and you eat less. That is healthy. In Indian food, the calories are relatively high and so is the fat content. This is especially true in the colder climates. In the hotter areas like southern India, people eat much lighter food because of the heat. The intensity of the weather and living conditions in general determine the spices that are good for the stomach in each of the states. People often travel to India where I can see them develop appetite problems and different diseases show in their blood as a kind of stimulation happens in the liver. They mistakenly attribute the symptoms to the water, which has the same amount of chlorine as anywhere else, according to Indian law.

The South Indian way of food preparation is mostly based on seasonal changes. A year is divided into four seasons of three months each. Each season there are changes, so we change our food according to what is compatible with the weather. Do not try to follow your constitution too much — that way you are controlled by the constitution. When you follow the weather patterns, you take control of yourself.

You can feel yourself change with dietary changes as you can feel the difference in your clothing. In the spring and summer, clothing is lighter; in autumn and winter, clothing is heavier. Similarly, we adjust our diet with the seasons. Because we are all human, we all have similar energy, but depending on the time we were born, we have certain differences. So we follow Nature. As Nature changes, we change with her. These principles apply to an average, healthy person. When a person becomes sick, then specific diets are required.

When I was visiting a museum in California, I pressed on buttons on a map and saw images of India and other countries of the world. Maps indicated where there is supposedly no disease, which is hard for me to believe. Disease and problems occur in the human body no matter where you are from. People in India have maintained good skin, which indicates health, even though India was portrayed as having disease. Disease means we do not have enough immunity. In my childhood, a man once came to the house to make compost for the plants. He had to dig in cow dung. When he came inside, I noticed he had a wound in his leg. According to Western theory, he should have been dead soon, but he was a perfectly healthy man with round muscles all over his body.

When I was sitting at a dinner table in Europe, we were watching a televised visit of that country's president to India. There was a shot that showed the prime minister of India and the president of the European country; then the TV showed a shot of a child taking a piece of bread from the mud and eating it. The journalist was showing that one of the most beautiful countries in the world, with some of the healthiest people, had a child in the dirt. I noticed that the child's eyes were sparkling and he was actually very healthy, despite the fact the journalist wanted to show India as a stereotype. It does not cost more than a few cents to have the healthiest food in the world. In a place like India, some of the cuisine is as perfectly balanced as good American cuisine.

Spice Up Your Life

There are twenty-eight regions in India and at least twenty-eight types of cuisine. Each region has its own traditional recipes. Each of the dishes is entirely unique.

Traditional Indian cuisine is not hot at all. In fact, it should not be hot; the effect of the black pepper or chili should be to slightly warm the body. We say that chili makes blood into water, and too much chili can dilute the toxins too much inside the veins. It is like starting with one glass of wine. After one, we start taking more and more and become addicted. Chili is also a kind of addiction. The heat is an overstimulation of the body in the same way that alcohol overstimulates the body. To the extent that we overstimulate the body, that is the extent to which we become addicted.

The greatest abundance of spices grown anywhere is in South India. Many cultures have used spices for medicinal purposes, including prescription medicines. For example, people use pepper as a remedy, along with other herbs, for even the most sensitive stomach. It is the perfect combining of spices that is important. One should never eat pepper when the stomach is irritated, but it is very effective with the correct combination of ingredients.

Indian cuisine has such different effects on our system. The Western digestive system is very vulnerable and sensitive, whereas the Indian digestive system is much stronger. Using the herbal combinations externally in the marma creams helps because the skin also has absorption and elimination. The marma teas are mild internal formulas for our arteries to absorb nutrients and our veins to remove toxins from the intestines. There are very few people who can easily digest Indian cuisine because of the spices, but applying the herbal combinations to the skin, complemented by the teas, creates the same benefits as taking the spices internally. The external and internal herbal effects are a complete stimulation.

Cleansing Diet

The action of the herbal teas and creams is more rapid and effective when a cleansing diet is followed. This is particularly advisable if your skin breaks out and you would like to clear it up as soon as possible. Eating brown rice and vegetables produces results in just a few days.

Boil 1 cup of rice in 2 cups of water. Prepare vegetables, such as carrots, asparagus, green beans, and broccoli. Boil the vegetables with double the amount of water. Drain the water. Add a little salt

Conclusion

There is one last thing I would like to say. Modern science has spent billions of dollars in research only to figure out that herbs can be useful for human well-being. This kind of knowledge is not a new discovery; it is very ancient and is untainted by politics. Great sages created this biotechnology for mankind in a past millennium and it still holds true today. Is it not our duty to save this intelligence for the next generations?

In every science, there is good and valuable knowledge. It is always necessary to adapt positive principles and keep them in our consciousness. What I speak of here is clearly science, the ancient ways of universal law which are beyond religious beliefs, fanaticism, or insecurity.

I am not interested in politics or religion. I really believe that no matter the community, people can achieve spiritual attainment. At that level, one can see people as equal, as there is no separation between humans in terms of belief systems. There is no need for separation between humans to protect our own insecurity. We only need to recognize how similar we are in the unity of universal life. Anyone who achieves this level looks at humans as one energy and God as One. That means success in reaching the goal of what these sciences are meant to accomplish - an evolution in light.

How much could it cost to preserve the wisdom of the ages? Perhaps it would cost the same as making some harmful chemicals? How much money do we spend to keep a few paintings in a museum — maybe a million dollars a year? With a good look at our priorities, we could release many of the burdens and expenditures in favor of beautifying our lives.

We travel millions of miles into space just to get some residual materials from another planet, which are radioactive anyway. We have this beautiful planet Earth with everything we need, so why not spend some money to rescue this ancient technology that can benefit the whole of mankind? The teachings of thousands of years not only show us a better quality of life, but also the way to die peacefully and gracefully as we transition to the next life.

What better museum could we build than one created for future generations to see and study the most ancient recorded wisdom of life and rejuvenation? I would like to invite each of you to come forward and join with me in researching and developing this project, to which I have dedicated my life's efforts.

To learn this knowledge has taken years of hard work. To share it with everyone is difficult for me to do alone. Please accept this precious natural wisdom into your lives and see the joy, success, and beauty that blossom in your world.

Marma Skincare
and Daily Routine

Please see figures 33 and 34 in the center of this book
[Marma Skincare products]

At night the body works to throw off the toxins that have accumulated during the day. In the morning, these toxins are resting on the skin's surface. The PURIFYING DAILY CLEANSER is very refreshing both morning and evening to cleanse impurities from the face. The pores are gently opened and ready for the nourishment of the appropriate herbal cream. The Purifying Daily Cleanser is also an excellent healing shave gel for men and women.

> N. M. of La Habra, California, had this to say about the cleanser:
> I have been evaluating cleansers for years. Joseph's Purifying Daily Cleanser is the best, very different in quality from the others. It's not gritty, but it cleans thoroughly. Also, there is a serenity that comes from using it that is hard to describe. It makes me feel good, while it cleans my skin perfectly.

> J. S. of San Diego, California, wrote the following after trying the cleanser:
> The Purifying Daily Cleanser is incredible. My face has never felt so clean. There is no residue at all — just smooth, clear skin with finer pores and a tighter feel.

The Nourishing Day Cream goes completely into my skin, moisturizing perfectly. Make-goes on beautifully afterwards. When I use the Purifying Daily Cleanser and Nourishing Day Cream together in the morning, I feel more alert for the day. It's sort of a calm awakening. My skin has gained a new, beautifully toned look in just a few weeks of application.

The cream for daytime contains herbs which activate certain energies that we need for the activities of the waking hours. When people apply the NOURISHING DAY CREAM, they say that their faces begin to look more vibrant and animated. The herbs restore the skin's own natural ability to hold moisture and form a defense against environmental impurities, keeping the skin protected and supple all day.

The Nourishing Day Cream also stimulates the energy channels on the face that direct the quality of digestion. Many clients have noticed their digestion improves with use of the facial creams even before they start taking the teas. As the energy channels open, the skin becomes smoother and clearer, and light comes to the face and eyes.

L. L. of Santa Barbara, California, used these words:
Joseph recommended a jar of his Nourishing Day Cream and I found it pleasant to use. There was no greasiness. It felt enlivening on my skin, not like a cover-up. Within three weeks of using the cream, the spot on my face sloughed off! My pores closed up and the lines diminished. My skin looked fresh and new as if I had used a chemical peel, but using the cream was as natural as watering a plant. My skin looks so good, I find I use very little make-up now.

L. R. of Huntington Beach, California, wrote:
My blotchy sunspots are all fading away and my skin tone is lighter and more even. I can't believe this cream! You smooth it on and your face smoothes out! I feel really good when I use this cream and my skin feels silky. I used to buy expensive department store creams because I have very dry skin. Now I use Joseph Kurian's creams because my skin stays moisturized all day. It works better than

anything else.

There is a parallel system for the REJUVENATING NIGHT CREAM that also synergizes the energy channels on the face with the body. At night we are more relaxed, and we experience a gentle cleansing in preparation for the new day. Our body works to rejuvenate itself, throwing off toxins and renewing and repairing cells. This rich formula supports the body's natural metabolic cycle, aiding its work to produce freshness in mind, body, and spirit.

While we gently sleep, the herbs in the Rejuvenating Night Cream work very gradually on the face to produce a cool, calm feeling. Sleep becomes deeper and more restful. The mind works at night to sort out all the data from the day's activities, which is stored in the lymphatic fluid. When toxins dominate the digestion, the lymphatic fluid creates stressful and negative dreams. Sleep quality is poor and one awakens with a puffy, unrested appearance. Traditional herbal science holds that correctly combined herbs allow the lymphatic fluid to purify. Many clients have commented that they experience a pleasant drowsiness with the application of the Rejuvenating Night Cream, making their transition to sleep natural. They awaken clear and refreshed. So the Nourishing Day Cream and Rejuvenating Night Cream complement and harmoniously balance each other.

> L. L. of Riverside, California said this about the Rejuvenating Night Cream:
> Since I started using the Rejuvenating Night Cream before bed, I have noticed the quality of my sleep has changed. It's sublime. The quality of my rest is very deep, and when I wake up and look at my face, the skin looks fresh like never before. Friends tell me I am glowing.

> P. M. of Mill Valley, California, works in front of a computer, as many of us do:
> Do you know what 'computer face' is? That's the tired face you get when you look at a computer screen all day. With my first application of Joseph's cream after a long day at the computer, I felt the fatigue and toxicity dissolve into pure relaxation.

The RENEWING EYE CREAM contains an even more penetrating herbal extract for the areas around the eyes. Since there are no sebaceous glands in that area, the skin is more vulnerable to developing age lines. The Renewing Eye Cream diminishes these telltale lines and protects against their further development.

> C. G. of Miami, Florida, began using the Renewing Eye Cream and said:
> When I first started using Marma Skincare, I realized the value of the herbal formulas. Then Joseph came out with the Renewing Eye Cream and I noticed after a while that my eyes felt a little sandy when I woke up in the morning. I was thinking of discontinuing the Eye Cream, when I realized that I had not been using my reading glasses for two weeks! It dawned on me that the herbs in the Eye Cream were really just cleansing the tissues and actually improving my eyesight.

> L. S. of Grand Prairie, Canada, was delighted with her results:
> I had cosmetic surgery on my eyes to remove the fat pads about nine years ago, and on my left eye there was a bump on the incision line. I have no idea if it was a stitch or scar tissue or what. I remember when he got to that spot, the doctor panicked and said, "You're bleeding too much." And then I bought the Eye Cream and the Travel Kit so I was using all the products, and within one week the bump just worked itself out. It was neat. I thought it was going to be there forever. I had heard that surgeon was really good and there would be no scars. But that bump was there for so long. I see it as a blessing because now that it's gone, I can run my hand over the area and it feels so smooth and healed.

Stimulation of the body's natural processes helps to clear the passage of the cells through the veins to the liver, where they are beautified and sent out. The electrical energy goes through the nerves to the outside of the body, and the physical elements go to the skin and tissues. When the **Stimulating Body Lotion** is turned upside down, without shaking, and put in the palm of our hand, we can feel a very light electric shock. This is the concentration of the electromagnetic current! We also have an aura of light, or electromagnetic current, that fills the body and emanates from the skin. When the STIMULATING BODY LOTION is applied to the skin, the herbal extracts synergistically connect to the current in the body to create a very special energy. This energy keeps stimulating the skin all day long.

The STIMULATING BODY LOTION prevents the formation of fat cells and helps the muscles to absorb nutrients, resulting in a dramatic firming action. According to tradition, the herbs in this formula normalize appetite as well. When Stimulating Body Lotion is applied all over the entire body, the energy which we have inside — the light, the electromagnetic current — starts to circulate throughout the body. These currents are activated and begin to travel along the subtle circuitry, clearing blockages and restoring a natural rate of flow.

The Stimulating Body Lotion enlivens the whole energy of a person. The reason we feel like eating again and again is that we become addicted to food when it is not recirculating properly or digesting properly. The biochemistry of nutrition is, therefore, not complete and we are still hungry even though we have eaten. We may partially digest our food, but the circulation of the energy flow is too slow, because the current which is created inside in our head with improper breathing is insufficient. Even then, though we may create this current, the electromagnetic current may not flow properly because of blockages in the marmas.

Along with nutritious food, along with nutritious pranic energy, the energy channels must remain open for the synthesis of the two. When the two types of nourishment do not mingle, the energy gets stuck in different parts of the body, especially in the stomach and thigh areas — a large supply of congested energy that has to be recirculated all over the body.

The distribution of this energy is assisted by the flexibility coming from exercise and also by stimulating the electromagnetic current. That is the secret of the Stimulating

Body Lotion. People say that as their acidity level comes down, they do not feel as hungry, although their appetites are improved. Their digestion starts to function better and their bodies reshape to a firmer and more youthful contour.

> M. K. of St. Louis, Missouri, made these comments about Marma creams:
> I love the way it makes my skin feel. I can literally see it rejuvenate before my eyes. After one month of being consistent with the Stimulating Body Lotion, I know I haven't lost weight, but my just-washed jeans are loose. It was like "Poof" after thirty days of being consistent. That's the second part of the magic formula. The first is Joseph and the second is consistency.
>
> After twenty years of antibiotics for my skin and still enjoying the sun, I was developing sunspots on my face. Now with Joseph's creams, I'm tanning differently. My tan looks much better and the sunspots are less. That's one reason why I have to have the Nourishing Day Cream.
>
> I have cellulite on my legs and that is less predominant now. Seeing results like that makes me want to use the product but it makes me want to do other good things for my body, too.
>
> L. M. of San Francisco, California, recently purchased Marma Skin Care:
> What I noticed on my face is that it's plumper. It smoothes it out. As you get older, the skin tends to thin. I love the Body Lotion when I rub it along my spine. I get a sense of well being that is quite lovely. It's so relaxing, it must be that energy channels are really opening up. Another thing I noticed is when I put the Body Lotion over my solar plexus area, there was a rather thick layer of fat that I was concerned about that is getting softened.

The Toning Cellulite Complex is the herbal solution to the condition of cellulite, whatever its cause. The concentrated formula in this lotion is to be used for specific areas of concern.

The Toning Cellulite Complex works to dissolve the excess coagulated layers so that the tissues are able to resume normal circulation and the skin can become smooth again.

J. B. of Piedmont, California attests to the positive effects:

The creams have become a part of my daily ritual, morning and evening. It's like surrounding myself with a mantle of light. I just love the smell. It's a wonderful way to start the day, as well as a great way to end it. It's relaxing in the evening, assists me in falling asleep. In the morning, it's energizing, get me going. When I use the cellulite cream, I definitely notice a difference. I purposely used it on certain parts of my body to see if there was a difference, and I noticed one. Within a fairly short period of time, the tone of my skin changed, the lines and the slight dimpling that was there have diminished tremendously. I'm not wearing any make-up and you can see just by using the cream, that my skin has an evenness to the tone and the texture.

There is a certain quality of light that I notice whenever I put it on. There's a certain glow. The cream really does assist my skin in becoming firmer. There were lines and dark circles under my eyes. Those have diminished. The tone of it is just more elastic and supple, felt confidence. My feeling that I'm able to face the day, whatever it's going to bring me, regardless of how stressful it is, I always feel that there's something about the quality of the product that enhances my being so that when I go out into the world, I just feel better about myself.

I really feel as though I'm doing something special for myself whenever I use the creams. There's a certain nurturing quality about them. I feel as though I'm treating myself well, and I see the results of it every time I look in the mirror. I just feel as though there is a certain glow about me that lasts throughout the day. Another wonderful thing I discovered about Joseph's creams is the hand & nail cream. I've been using it for quite some time now, and the quality of my skin is much softer.

T. J. of Atlanta, Georgia, was really quite pleased with
her results:
This is great! The Toning Cellulite Complex is natural
liposuction. I was actually entertaining the notion of
what must be a traumatic procedure to the body. Now,
all I have to do is put on some cream that smells and
feels good. How can I ever thank you?

The SOOTHING HAND & NAIL CARE is luxurious relaxation for
hands and feet. Hands and feet take on an aged appearance
sooner than do other parts of the body due to blockages caused
by hard use, injury, and neglect. Formulated for the greater
number of bones in those areas, Soothing Hand & Nail Care is
known to assist the calcium process. Nails and cuticles regain
their attractive appearance and excess calcium deposits
dissolve, growing out through the nails. The legendary Kaya
Kalpa herbs make nails glossy, smooth, and strong. It is very
beneficial to apply the cream to both hands and feet because of
the reflexology points that radiate renewed energy throughout
the body. Massaging the Soothing Hand & Nail Care into these
points, morning and evening, produces remarkable changes
toward young, supple skin.

K. M. of Reno, Nevada, can show her hands again:
My nails were so unsightly that to be in public was a
living nightmare. I was always hiding my hands for fear
that someone would notice. Doctors told me that I
would most likely lose my nails and there was nothing
to be done. Thank God that Joseph Kurian has a better
answer! My nails have become so strong and long and
they never even break. Artificial nails with chemicals
that destroy the nail bed are obsolete. Just get the Marma
Hand Care.

M. C. of Daly City, California, is a massage therapist. She
said:
Oh, it's wonderful. I feel something is really happening.
My skin feels more sensitive and I'm aware of my body as

a whole. I can feel the channels opening up. I feel I'm coming into my body in a gentle, more sensual way. The creams and the oils are really lovely. I appreciate the nurturance of the formulas. Using them on the feet starts a delicious relaxation traveling through my body.

Marma Teas

The healing properties of herbs are a natural support system for well-being. Repeated use of the Marma Teas gives the potential of thoroughly cleansing the physiology and activating the body's own rejuvenating mechanisms. Taken twice daily for internal purification, the teas strengthen and balance the energy system at the source, while the herbal creams bring the light of your life force to the surface of the body.

The set of teas contains a month's supply of herbs to rejuvenate the marma. Missing a day occasionally does not interfere with the benefits. Simply continue the next day. Cleansing your system with the teas is very beneficial to reestablish inner balance and outer beauty. Marma Teas greatly enhance the benefits of the creams. The herbs and knowledge are rare and precious. Anyone who follows the simple instructions will experience results seldom available in our history.

New Products

For a more invigorating cleansing, the Joseph Kurian HERBAL FACIAL SCRUB can be used instead of the Purifying Cleanser. This non-abrasive scrub is good for occasional use when you feel like a deeper cleansing and stimulation of the energy centers on the face.

Once a week, find a little extra time to do a Joseph Kurian HERBAL FACIAL MASK. Based on the knowledge of herbal energetics, this mask is uncommonly refreshing. People who have had the Herbal Facial Mask say that it not only brings a fresh luster to their skin, but also adds the pleasure of energy radiating throughout their bodies as the facial marmas are opened by the resonant herbal combination.

The Herbal Facial Mask is based on the same concept as people use in Indian temples when they apply different kinds of paste on their face. In various states in India, there are certain days of the week when people apply herbal paste on their face in order to purify themselves. This is done as a ritual — when we go to see the God, we need to purify ourselves internally and externally. Only then can we really connect to the light which is coming from God as well as producing light inside of us. The Facial Mask and Facial Scrub are both based on the same concept, without losing any aspect of the age-old tradition.

KAMINI SENSUALITY BODY LOTION and KAMA HERBAL TABLETS are a specialty set that bring to life the aphrodisiac mentioned in the amorous text of the ancient Kama Sutra. There was a time when people believed that sexuality was sacred and spiritual. They discovered effective herbal combinations that could promote the passion of sexual energy in order to fulfill enjoyment. In the olden time, they could integrate this spiritual/sexual energy with the seeking of enlightenment.

The Kamini Sensuality Body Lotion is a natural herbal blend in a silky lotion that gently stimulates life force energy, the key to sexuality in both women and men. In combination with the Kama Herbal Tablets, the lotion makes skin more flexible and elastic. The energy in the body can concentrate in the sexual organs as well as circulate throughout the body. For women, Kamini Body Lotion can help to alleviate cramps in the lower abdominal area prior to menstruation. For both men and women, the natural herbs of the lotion and tea gently stimulate passionate desire and enhance romantic, sensual feelings.

People who have acne can diminish or even eliminate the condition with the set of ACNE CREAM and ACNE TABLETS. Acne has been a challenge even for advanced medicine, and has

Fire	Aries Ruby Charisma	Leo Coral Inner Strength	Sagittarius Topaz Happiness
Earth	Taurus Pearl Joy	Virgo Emerald Progress	Capricorn Sapphire Protection
Air	Gemini Emerald Tranquility	Libra Diamond Wisdom	Aquarius Sapphire Love
Water	Cancer Pearl Security	Scorpio Coral Brilliance	Pisces Topaz Optimism

increased with the depletion of ozone. The last seven years of my research have successfully helped client volunteers with this powerful enemy to the skin. Calming and corrective, natural herbal blends in the cream and tablets penetrate deeply beneath the skin's protective layer to cleanse and balance sebaceous glands. These are exceptionally effective formulas from the ancient health sciences of India.

In Chapter Eleven, you learned about the marvelous **Rejuvenation Program** involving energy work and warm oils that is patterned after the royal treatment enjoyed by kings and queens of India. In ancient time, the miraculous benefits of precious stones were essential in the advanced rejuvenation treatments. The royalty wore gemstones on different parts of their body not only as beautiful jewelry, but because gems have beneficial powers derived from the planets or the sun. With careful selection and specific design, each stone was chosen and set to correspond with energy centers of the body. In this manner, the gemstone energies strengthened the person's energy field with higher vibrational frequencies.

Royalty retained masters to help them ascertain their physical state and advise them when it would be best to wear certain jewels and not others. Calculating the position of the planets and the potential negative effects, the masters could prevent the negative and accent the positive energies by accurately balancing the whole physiology of their royal patrons.

The GEMSTONE MASSAGE OILS are a self-care version of this ancient gemstone technology. Designed for the four different elements in astrology, precious gems are combined for the energetic benefits of air, fire, earth, and water.

The ancient method of using gemstone energies also fortifies the herbal formulas in the oil. This concept has been very expensive, yet it was highly regarded in past history as an incomparable method of maintaining charisma in a person. An exhilarating and penetrating warm oil massage with any of the Gemstone Massage Oils produces lustrous skin, clear thoughts, and tranquil emotions as the gemstone energies harmonize planetary and personal vibrations.

Daily Routine and Guidelines

Aware of all the challenges and adjustments influencing your daily choices, I am showing you the art of Marma Science and giving you the support of Marma Skincare to help you become your naturally positive self.

Change is one of the few constants in life, so we need a balance point for continuity and guidance. A movie does not stay on one frame and a song does not remain on one note. These herbal formulas and the simplified routines provide a theme for this balance. You can learn to navigate through the daily currents and stay focused on the evolution of your life. One of my goals has been to make this as effortless as possible for you while you gain deep, rewarding benefits. Take a look at a typical day:

MORNING

When you first awaken in the morning, do the NSK (Nadi Sutra Kriya) and one or two breathing exercises. This will stimulate and balance your chakras and energy system in a matter of minutes. Then you can do your morning meditation with greater clarity.

Make a routine of brushing your teeth, (shaving every day if you are a man), performing your ablutions, and finishing with your shower. Taking a shower in the morning wakes up your whole system. Before taking a shower to clean your skin, you can give yourself an oil massage, or abhyanga. If you are someone who likes to use warm oil or someone who would like to learn, it is very good for stimulating the marma system. After that, take your shower and use the Marma Skincare as your protective cloak for the day. The skincare products work at the fundamental level of subtle energy, so they are good for anyone and everyone.

The Purifying Daily Cleanser cleans and refreshes your face in a minute or two. Wash it off and apply the Nourishing Day Cream. The Day Cream gently energizes you for your daily activities. Choose the Renewing Eye Cream, if you like, for the sensitive skin around the eyes. Use the Toning Cellulite Complex for specific areas of the body that need to be reduced. A quick moisturizing with Stimulating Body Lotion all over from your neck down feels like an energy shower after your morning shower. You are ready for whatever comes your way.

The Soothing Hand Care is equally soothing for your feet. If you work with your hands all day, you can reapply it as often as necessary.

MIDDAY

When the opportunity presents itself during the day, choose a mudra and breathing exercise to revive your energy. This could be during a break at the office or when you stop to rest during a long drive. For example, if you are feeling tense, do the nerve marma mudra with the thumb and middle finger to relax. Remember, you literally have these techniques at your fingertips.

EVENING

If you are going to a party after work, you can freshen up with the Cleanser and apply the Day Cream for activating energy. Before bed, the Cleanser and Rejuvenating Night Cream will soothe your system and lull you to sleep. This is a good time to use the Hand Care on your feet, with their reflexology points. Some people prefer to do an oil massage at night, which is perfectly all right if you find that it is not too stimulating.

Oil Massage

I recommend an oil massage maybe three times a week to help your body become more flexible and increase your circulation. Do not leave any oil on your body more than twenty minutes because our skin needs to breathe in much the same way as our nose.

There are three oils I recommend which balance body, mind, and spirit. Each has a well-balanced herbal formula to stimulate the marmas. Oil # 3 is for body, Oil # 7 is for mind, and Oil # 8 is for spirit. Each bottle of oil is sufficient for three applications during one week. When you go through this routine, you can feel a cleaning taking place with Oil # 3 as your physical body, the vascular system, starts to become more flexible. Your movements are much easier if you are doing any sports or exercise because your cardiovascular system starts to function better.

Oil # 7 works on the mind, the nervous system. During this week, you will see your mind clearing out many old thoughts that were kept inside. Very lightly, the limiting thought patterns come out and are released. When you continue for a certain time, your mind will be much more clear; it will be much easier to think and do things better.

Oil # 8 works on the spirit, which is the endocrine system. While doing the oil treatments, you can feel happiness and joy increasing. Things become easier in your life; people respond to you more positively. The herbs in the oil are a combination of lavender, geranium, sage, and other aromatic extracts. Many of these herbs are very familiar and have been used from the ancient time.

Along with the oils, we should also take a combination of herbs which is designed to stimulate the whole marma system. You only need to take a tablespoon two times a day — morning and evening — for twenty-one days. Each of the three weeks in the twenty-one days corresponds to the body, mind, and spirit. The first week is the body; the second week is the mind; the third week is the spirit. When you work with the herbs, you will have even more beneficial experience than with the oils alone. It is best to start this program of herbs and oils from the beginning of every month and finish it in three weeks. Take at least one week's rest from the herbs and start again. This can continue for up to seven months. This program can be done more intensively for deep cleansing. For that we should take off no more than the minimum of one week between the programs.

The herbal blends are recommended according to our astrological and planetary positions. There are many practices like mantras, meditation, and breathing that can be done in conjunction with the Herbal Program. Then only can it completely work on every level of body, mind, and spirit. I have been doing this for the last many years.

The Healing Program

After a series of Herbal Programs, the lighter blockages will be released and then the major blockages can be addressed. Then is a good time to have a **Healing Program**. The Healing Program is seven private sessions of marma restoration during one week. This is an extremely subtle, yet powerful, clearing of blockages and stimulation of your own life force. The Healing Program works on the issues that the herbs cannot reach. Some of the blockages are very deep and the herbs alone cannot open the marmas. With my knowledge of the energy system, I have been able to help open up the blockages for many people. This methodology is very hard on both people — the healer and the patient. Lots of emotional issues previously withheld come out very intensely and could possibly penetrate through my aura. To protect from them, I do special practices like meditation and Nadi Sutra Kriya. Another technique is called Veerya Mudra. These create a shield between healer and the patient.

Here is how it works. The Healing Program done in one week or over a long weekend. Seven treatment sessions with transformational energy work channel vital energy through the body. This stimulation removes blockages and opens the pathways for healing energy to flow freely. During this process, I note the individual factors such as breath, pulse, capacity of the heart, and body thickness. The removal of toxins is accelerated and the delivery of nutrients and information is enhanced.

This work is an intensive, highly developed method of energy release, which produces feelings of exhilaration and blissful freedom. People notice an increased sense of well-being, improved skin tone, vibrant hair, clear eyes and healthy nails. Digestion improves and breathing becomes easier. The blood is oxygenated and energy levels much higher. Anyone receiving this beautiful shakti will feel a certain peaceful confidence.

Blockages ordinarily occur in the energy channels of the human body from emotional or physical traumas, manifesting in such physical symptoms as a pinched nerve, a slipped disk, poor circulation, congestion of the organs, anxiety, depression, and neuroses. The Healing Program releases energy blockages on a very deep and subtle level so the life force can freely circulate.

When the pathways are opened, the marma centers are activated to function in their capacity as natural switching regulators for the current coming from the chakras. The marmas form an interconnecting pattern of energy triangles throughout the body. If the chain is broken, the balance in the entire system is upset. Compare it to the electrical circuitry in a house. If one switch is not working properly, the lights will not function.

With the proper repairs, the electromagnetic energy flows uninterrupted along the circuitry of the human body and the light of shakti illuminates our entire being. Once the energy channels are open, the herbal preparations are even more effective, as they also resonate with the subtle energies of the whole body. We are renewed by our own natural healing process.

> H. Z. of San Diego, California, came to Joseph on an intuitive hunch:
> This was a very successful session for me. Joseph got rid of a big blockage. I had what the chiropractor called arthritis. All the tingling is gone. My arm and shoulder don't ache. I think that's pretty phenomenal, myself, particularly since I've been going to chiropractors on and off for the last year and they weren't able to get rid of it. Symptoms like that are their specialty and there's even a question of misdiagnosis involved. Joseph said the tingling in my arm was the nerve impulse trying to get through the blockage and the arthritis was the calcified deposits on the tendons from the two shoulder areas attaching to the spinal column at the cervical region. The third and fourth days of the session were very, very intensive, but definitely worth it.
>
> As usual, the herbalized oils conveyed the changes to the energy body. What I have the feeling he is doing or what the oils do is they activate the astral body in conjunction with what he's doing physically and enable him to affect your physiology on that level also. So the repair is not just organic or just with the tissues, but he's actually harmonizing the system at the level of the energy body, the marmas, simultaneously. It's the herbalized oils that make this connection possible and it was the cognition of the ancient rishis who perceived this technique.
>
> Otherwise, nobody has the training or sensitivity to cognize the potential for healing when used in the right ways. He started to learn this when he was a kid and developed his own awareness of it with the help of his teachers. Through conducting his own research, he has continued to refine and develop the applicability of it,

as well as seeing to the continued cultivation of the herbs according to the ancient formulations.

He's exactly what he claims to be — the inheritor and the person carrying on this ancient tradition and healing art at the level at which it was originally cognized and envisioned. The masters recognized his potential and passed onto him what was passed onto them, which was not only the intellectual knowledge but the practical scientific ability to practice what he knows.

When the marmas are cleared, a heightened level of consciousness is created inside, which radiates a very clear aura, or electromagnetic current. The aura — which might be compared to the reception and transmission qualities of modern electronics — radiates the light of shakti, the pure and natural life energy. Beauty and charisma are a reflection of the aura, which has to be developed from the synergistic balance of the three parts of the human system. The next level is advanced rejuvenation.

Spontaneous Renewal
When it is convenient for you, treat yourself with an Herbal Facial Mask or the Marma Facial Massage. Anytime you use my herbal formulas, your energy is enhanced. When you feel good, you look good. When you know you look good, you feel even better. The stimulation of your subtle energies integrates your mind and body and aligns your spiritual strength. Your potential opens up; you can actualize your goals. When you are fully functioning as an individual, there is a chemistry of charisma that will attract positive people and experiences into your life. This attraction opens up new opportunities for enjoyment and success.

The NSK is especially significant as a secret tool for success. The Nadi Sutra Kriya is always there for you when you need to center yourself and focus your strength. The NSK is powerful because it unlocks the third chakra, where many people hold their fears. The only requirement is you and your knowing how to do it. When you find yourself facing a challenging situation, use the NSK. As your energy channels open, your pathway to success opens.

Whenever you need to calm yourself, find a little time and space for meditation with the Marma Mantra. Choose the finger mudra to balance the part of you that is holding back. Here is a reminder:

When you need to breathe deeper, use the thumbs and forefingers.
When you are nervous, use the thumbs and middle fingers.
When you are tired, use the thumbs and ring fingers.
When you are emotional, use the thumbs and little fingers.

Seasonal Renewal

I would like to offer my **Energy Reading** as an occasional support. You can call my office to schedule an appointment. I suggest this on a seasonal basis to correspond with the flow of changing influences. Once in a while, a consultation is very helpful to learn how you are progressing and what adjustments can be made to maximize your energy. During an Energy Reading, we find exactly where the blockages are located. Many people have even become well just by knowing what it is exactly and where and how it started. After a while of doing the meditation by themselves with my instruction, the body healed itself.

This is especially true of couples who have been very romantic in the beginning and continued for many years. Suddenly everything changes and they become enemies to each other. This could be just a planetary influence or it could be a marma blockage. It can even result from a movie they watched that triggered childhood memories to surface and change their attitudes. The situation can be corrected by finding out what exactly caused the rift and how they can return to their romantic life again. The custom herbal blends in the Herbal Program I recommend at the reading can specifically work on those issues.

The **Harmonizing Herbal Program** that I recommend is chosen to successively clear the marma layers in order of priority for your personal energy pattern. I will provide you with herbal recommendations to follow through each month. This is a self-care program of herbal blends and herbalized oils that you can do at home for three weeks, then wait at least one week before continuing with the next program.

During the three weeks, the herbal blends are taken morning

and evening, just a tablespoon at a time, before and after meals so the delicate chemistry of the stomach is balanced to receive and assimilate nutrition. People feel so much better when their digestion is working properly. They find they need less of the supplements they were taking because of poor assimilation. Beyond digestion, the energetic properties of the herbal blends permeate the different marma layers, dissolving blockages and freeing the energy flow.

While the herbs are working from the inside, the herbs in the oils are penetrating from the outside. The oil treatment is done only three times a week, not every day. The procedure is to apply the warm oil generously, covering the head and body, leaving it on for no more than twenty minutes. You can use this time to massage the oil into your marmas, or do some breathing exercises with mudras. The heat from the skin opens the pores, allowing the penetration of the herbal extract. The feeling of deep, soothing comfort is an experience you will come to enjoy as a luxury.

The Herbal Program is not something that has to be done for the rest of your life, but at least once in your life it's wise to clean the seven chakras and seven layers of your body. Seven months of the Herbal Program can clear much of the blockage that otherwise remains lodged, even though you try to have a healthy lifestyle. My clients are constantly remarking that the herbs work where nothing else would break through. They have memories surface that they have not thought of in years, which are released painlessly. This is something for all of us — a natural gift of energy cleansing.

Advanced Renewal

Your body has its own intelligence and ability to heal. The mind needs to be integrated with the body. The finer substance of Spirit needs clear channels to enter. I have been able to rejuvenate thousands of clients in many nations with this methodology. Cleaning out the deeper layers of your body requires an ability to reach the sensitive, subtle level, where blockages begin. In the new world, people will once again think of the most fundamental level as Spirit, which is expressed in mind and body.

After the Herbal and Healing Programs, you can think about

having the Rejuvenation Program. There, you can achieve the maximum rejuvenation and clear your cells. The very foundation of the subtle energy body is rebuilt and the freedom from past limitations can only be described as a blessing of divine grace. A similar week-long format as the Healing Program, the Rejuvenation Program offers the exponential benefits of specially processed gemstones and the ancient knowledge of Kaya Kalpa, which I have rediscovered. This is the most potent rejuvenation of all the wonderful traditions of India.

My **Rejuvenation Program** is designed for people who want the results faster than the Healing Program. According to people's experience, one Rejuvenation Program is equal to seven Healing Programs. Very effective and powerful knowledge goes into this concentrated renewal, clearing the way for a wonderful new life of health and beauty. This system of rejuvenation is a distillation of knowledge from all the sciences, parallel to the process of extracting the precious nectar from the plants and the gemstones. The philosophy and methodology of the Rejuvenation with Kaya Kalpa techniques are explained in greater detail in Chapter 12.

You are welcome to join me at workshops and seminars that I have in various beautiful locations. Some of them are for training professionals at spas and healing centers. Others are teachings of the NSK and Indian Martial Arts. You will meet people with a similar desire to evolve and find joy in their lives. The search for answers and the recognition of universal truths are a happy adventure when you find the right direction. All these programs I have designed are for people like you. I am following this advice myself as I go through life with tensions and challenges like anyone else. I hope that your Spirit will be uplifted to carry your mind and body toward more love and greater beauty.

GLOSSARY

abhyanga - oil massage.

ajna - desire to go beyond the forms of existence to enlightenment; associated with the sixth chakra.

akasha - element of ether or space; the field of existence which supports the manifestation of matter. It represents the principles governing space and distance that create the separateness of objects.

ama - physical impurities remaining in the body after digestion.

anahata - pivotal energy level between the material and spiritual, transition from the body and ego to love and selflessness; associated with the fourth chakra.

apas - element of water; represents the principles governing the liquid state of matter.

arbhutam - cancer

Ayur Veda - Science of Life; Indian system of health through natural balance; dates back thousands of years, written records beginning 5000 years ago.

brahma - absolute consciousness.

chakra - one of seven major marmas located along the spine; generates energy at the most subtle level of the nervous system; each chakra governs different principles of consciousness.

chinu mudra - finger position holding thumb and forefinger together on each hand; opens energy channels for easier, deeper breathing.

chundu marma - Dhanur Vedic battle technique of directing energy through a pointed finger; powerful method of distance attack.

curcuma - green vegetable used in the summertime.

Dhanur Veda - Science of Defense; strength on the battlefield; ancient knowledge since applied to the healing arts.

dhatu - one of seven tissue layers of the body.

dhyana - sublime state of meditation.

Dravada - ancient Indian civilization integral to the culture of Marma Science and all Vedic Sciences; all of India's sciences come from the Dravidian culture.

doshas - Vata (air), Pitta (fire), and Kapha (water) in Ayur Veda; bodily forces constantly balancing the five elements in physical form; three subtle forces governing the activities and functions of the body.

electromagnetic current - range of frequencies of electromagnetic radiation extending from gamma rays to radio waves and including visible light.

ether - rarefied element of the heavens held to permeate all space and transmit electromagnetic waves.

gada - heavy wooden mace used in Indian martial arts.

glow - visible auric vitality emanating from a person's countenance.

guru - spiritual and intellectual guide; mentor; acknowledged leader.

Gurukkal - title granted someone who has achieve the highest level of Dhanur Veda; literally, "One who knows."

homa - ritual of purification by burning certain herbs.

ida - left nostril and the breath that flows through it; energy channel from the nose to the base of the spine.

Kalaripayat - ancient form of Indian martial art recognized for strength and flexibility.

Kali Yuga - one of four ages of evolution in the Vedic system (Satya Yuga, Dvapara Yuga, Treta Yuga, and Kali Yuga). Kali Yuga is influenced by confusion; period of destructive mentality and negativity; we are in this gray period now.

Kama Sutra - Indian sexual treatise, dating from the 1st to the 4th centuries A.D., expounding on sexual etiquette, principles of pleasure and religious expression of the eternal dance of regeneration.

kalpa vrisha - term meaning "everything has a use," e.g., the coconut tree.

kapha - dosha representing the water principle; force governing bodily processes of cooling such as the vascular system.

Kathakali - elegant, classical dance form evolved from Kalaripayat.

Kaya Kalpa - deep, cellular rejuvenation practiced since ancient times in India; the culmination of the knowledge of gemstones, astrology, mantric power, and the powers of cosmic energy and pranic energy.

kundalini - spiritual energy present at the base of the spine that can be awakened to move up through the chakras to the crown chakra of enlightenment.

Mahabharata - one of the Vedic scriptures most important to India because it serves as a literary reflection of India's spiritual essence; mythic epic describing the battle of human physiology and human psychology.

mahamarma - major marma; chakra.

mahamudra - major mudra; e.g., Nadi Sutra Kriya.

Malayalam - ancient language of India directly derived from Sanskrit; contains 56 letters and is spoken in Kerala.

mandala - sacred art of patterns and colors reflecting the finer levels of sound and light; geometric designs used in uplifting contemplation

manipura - desire for success, wealth, power, longevity; manifestations of the same in the material world; contentment with success; associated with the third chakra.

manja marma - the marma located beneath the ear.

mantra - sacred sounds used in meditation to open energy channels and raise vibrational levels.

mantravadam - the science of mantras.

marma - an all-encompassing term for life force itself, as well as the pattern of channels through which it passes.

Marma Science - the study and practical knowledge of the energy circuitry and the nature of universal laws of energy; applied science of opening energy channels.

Marma Shastra - treatise on the treatment of marmas, written by Agasthya Muni.

Marma Sutra - palm leaf manuscripts recording knowledge of marmas from the oral tradition.

mastabhi - herbal blend that clears the marmas of the ears, chest, and navel mudra - positioning and pose of the body or hands to facilitate the completion of an energy circuit; practice used in meditation to awaken energy

muladhara - energy of the first chakra associated with basic biological needs of security and physical comfort.

NSK (Nadi Sutra Kriya) - simple yet powerful exercises to strengthen and balance one's own energy system; based on ancient warriors' preparation for battle.

nabhi marma - second chakra; area of convergence of 72,000 nerves of the body.

nadis - subtle energy channels conducting pranic force in and out of the physical body, closely linked with the nervous system.

Nadraja - god of knowledge

Om - sacred sound of eternity; essential mantra.

Om Nava Shivaya - sacred mantra meaning "I honor the Divine within me," in supplication to Shiva, the "Compassionate One" for dissolving obstacles to higher spirituality. These sounds directly correspond to the five organs; repeating the mantra stimulates the five organs.

otto kol - short, curved stick used in the Indian martial arts.

Pancha Mahabhutam - Sanskrit for "five great elements" referring to the universal belief that the world is composed of ether, air, fire, water, and earth.

photosensitive - capable of responding to sunlight.

pingali - right nostril and the breath that flows through it; energy channel from the nose to the base of the spine.

pitta - "fire" dosha representing the metabolic processes requiring heat, such as the endocrine system.

Prakriti - the creative Mother principle; the feminine of the eternal opposites.

prana - component of sunlight recognized as the vital force that enters the body with the breath.

pranayama - yogic breathing techniques for body/mind/spirit well-being practiced in India for thousands of years.

prithivi - the element of earth, representing the principles governing the solid states of matter.

Purusha- the unchanging Father principle; the masculine of the eternal opposites.

puja - purification of the atmosphere of an area in preparation for ritual, involving the burning of herbs, or homa.

ragas - musical progressions in Indian music composed for spiritual effects.

Raja Yogum - the luck to be a King; someone born with that potential.

sadhu - holy person choosing a simple life

sahasara - Self-realization or enlightenment; associated with the seventh chakra, the thousand-petaled lotus.

shakti - inner light born of a pure spiritual nature.

siddhi - mantric power for spiritual perfection.

Sri - title of an eminent person.

sthana - marma located on the chest, connected to the thymus.

Susruta Vagabada - treatise on the theoretical understanding of marmas, by Charaka.

svadhisthhana - desire for procreation and harmonious relationships; associated with the second chakra.

tantra - ancient Indian system of expanding awareness with methods from various sciences and philosophies; "to weave" a new self with concentrated energy; tantric yoga finds spirituality through sexuality.

tejas - fire element representing the principles which transform matter from one state to the next gaseous or other state of matter.

tridosha - unity of the three doshas—vata (air), pitta (fire), and kapha (water).

urumi - pliant sword belt used as a weapon in Kalaripayat to unfurl like a whip.

vaidya - physician

vagus nerve - one of the main nerves centrally located between the shoulder blades.

vajrasana - sitting or kneeling position with a straight spine for meditation exercises.

vata - "air" dosha governing all principles of the body governing movement, as in the nervous system.

vayu - element of air representing the principles of the gaseous state of matter.

Vedas - ancient Sanskrit scriptures of India delineating the laws of the human and divine universe; revelations from God cognized by the mystic seers and yogis.

veerya mudra pranayama - breathing exercise to strengthen internal light and connect the chakras with the marmas.

vishuddha - desire for deep knowledge of life and discrimination of truth from non-truth; associated with the sixth chakra.

yoga - to join, as in union with God; system of spiritual practice to calm the mind, balance the body, and develop awareness.

ABOUT THE AUTHOR

Joseph Kurian

Joseph Kurian is a gifted healer and marma master from Kerala, India. Synthesizing the energy technology of the Vedic Sciences and Kalaripayat, the highly evolved Indian martial art, he specializes in Kaya Kalpa, the knowledge of beauty and longevity.

After living in Europe for seven years and operating a distinguished beauty clinic in Paris, he has been giving energy readings and rejuvenation programs in the United States for the last ten years. Based in San Francisco, Joseph is president and formulator of Marma Skincare.

To reach Joseph Kurian, please call 1-800-565-6393, or e-mail him at lib@marma.com. Please also visit his website, located at www.marma.com.